# Good Food
# for Mums

amlyn

# Good Food for Mums

Sara Lewis

This book is dedicated to my two lovely children, Alice and William, and their father Andrew for making it all possible.

First published in Great Britain in 2002 by Hamlyn
a division of Octopus Publishing Group Limited
2–4 Heron Quays
London E14 4JP

ISBN 0600 60416 0

British Library Cataloguing-in-Publication Data
A catalogue record for this book is available from the British Library.

Printed and bound in China

The publisher has taken all reasonable care in the preparation of this book but the information it contains is not intended to take the place of treatment by a qualified medical practitioner.

## NOTES

Standard level spoon measures are used in all recipes
1 tablespoon = one 15 ml spoon
1 teaspoon = one 5 ml spoon

Both metric and imperial measurements are given for the recipes. Use one set of measures only, not a mixture of both.

Ovens should be preheated to the specified temperature. If using a fan-assisted oven, follow the manufacturer's instructions for adjusting the time and temperature. Grills should also be preheated.

A few recipes include nuts and nut derivatives. Anyone with a known nut allergy must avoid these. It is advisable for people with known allergic reactions to nuts and nut derivatives and those who may be potentially vulnerable to these allergies, such as pregnant and nursing mothers, to avoid dishes made with nuts and nut oils. It is also prudent to check the labels of pre-prepared ingredients for the possible inclusion of nut derivatives.

Free-range medium eggs should be used unless otherwise stated.

Pepper should be freshly ground unless otherwise specified.

The Department of Health advises that pregnant women should avoid liver, pâté, unpasteurised dairy produce, mould-ripened soft cheeses, such as Brie and Camembert, and uncooked or lightly cooked dishes made with eggs.

# Contents

# a diet for life

If you are planning a baby or have recently discovered that you are pregnant, now is the time to reflect on the way that you live your life and the foods that you eat. It is a great opportunity to look ahead during this very special time for you and your partner, and to new beginnings.

Surprising new research in both the United Kingdom and the United States has concluded that what you eat before conception, as well as during pregnancy, may influence the health of your baby in the long term. Researchers have discovered that some diseases, such as coronary heart disease, stroke, osteoporosis and diabetes, may not be a result of poor genes or an unhealthy lifestyle but could have their roots in foetal development. In the United States, it's known as "foetal programming" and suggests that the health we enjoy throughout our lives is shaped by the pregnancy that formed us. Professor Barker from Southampton University in the United Kingdom first pioneered this idea and is now backed by a 200-strong team sponsored by the Medical Research Council in Britain to develop it further. 'We used to think that your heart may fail because it was worn out, now we need to find out if it failed because it wasn't very well made!' If the researchers are right in their conclusions that too much emphasis has been placed on the importance of our genetic make-up in the past, then what a mum-to-be eats in pregnancy or pre-pregnancy has never been more important. For example, researchers have found that malnutrition in the first few months of pregnancy may damage the messages sent to the baby's brain that control appetite, which could lead to obesity in adult life. If a baby is very small, then its undersized kidneys will make it difficult to regulate blood pressure efficiently, thus possibly leading to high blood pressure in later life; while a lack of calcium may affect bone structure throughout life.

Don't let these statistics scare you. Eating a well-balanced, healthy and varied diet is not difficult and should supply all the nutrients necessary for the healthy development of your baby. Furthermore, far from being frightening, this information enables every would-be parent to give their baby the very best possible start in life through the foods they eat.

Over the next few chapters, this book outlines what constitutes a healthy diet, which foods to include and those to be wary of. Plus, there are lots of helpful tips on pre-conceptual care, right through to preparing for the birth of your baby and afterwards. There are also easy-to-prepare recipes that help you to put the advice and guidelines into practice, with super quick suppers, main meal salads and simple slow-cook meals – not forgetting healthy puds!

*Sara Lewis*

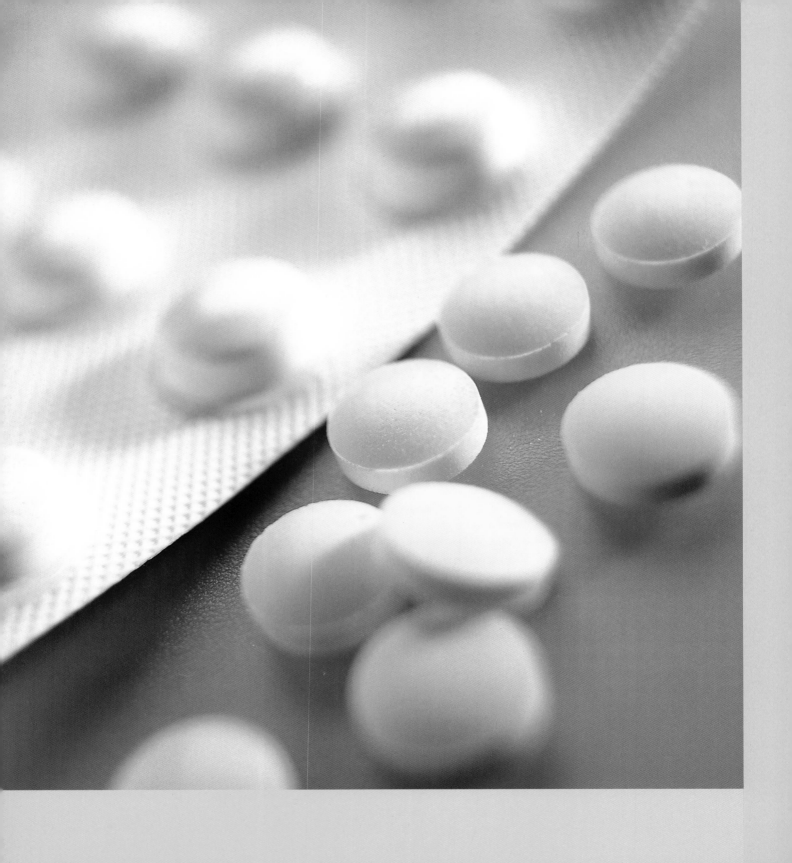

# PRE-CONCEPTION

With efficient birth control, having a baby these days is very much a planned and personal decision. Similarly, when preparing for the birth of your child how you live your life is very much down to you, but it is important to note that missed meals, late nights and hastily grabbed junk food may well take their toll on you and your unborn child. Now is the time to reflect on your lifestyle and get your body into shape from the inside out.

# getting in shape

Planning a baby is a great opportunity to take a fresh look at the way you and your partner live your lives – do you work too hard or feel persistently stressed? Do you drink too much on a regular basis? What about that half-hearted attempt to give up smoking! Or those meals you've missed because you've just been too busy to stop for a proper lunch!

The way in which you look after your body can affect your ability to conceive. A woman who is poorly nourished and either underweight or overweight is much less likely to conceive than one who is fit and healthy. There is also growing evidence that a baby's health in later life is linked to the health of the mother, not only during childhood but also around the time of conception.

Even though your pregnancy may not have been planned, it's never too late to review your lifestyle and really get yourself into shape. The following tips will help considerably, some are more relevant to those who are hoping to conceive, while others will apply to those who are already in the early stages of pregnancy.

# TOP TEN TIPS

**1 Review your lifestyle** 3–6 months before you hope to conceive your child.

**2 Start taking a folic acid supplement.** Research has proved that this vital vitamin can greatly reduce the chance of giving birth to a baby with neural tube defects, such as spina bifida. In this condition, one or more bones in the spine fails to develop, resulting in spinal cord and nerve damage.

Although folic acid is found naturally in green vegetables, some pulses and yeast extract, diet alone cannot provide sufficiently large amounts. Start taking a 400 mg folic acid supplement on a daily basis from the time you start trying to conceive until the 12th week of pregnancy. Even if you don't take folic acid before conceiving, it's worth starting as soon as you find out that you are pregnant. There are no side effects to folic acid, since the body naturally gets rid of any excess, and supplements are widely available from pharmacists, large supermarkets and health food shops. (See page 22 on how to increase folic acid in your diet.)

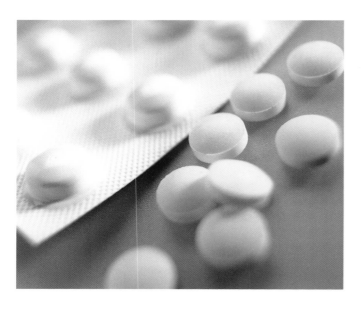

**3 Boost vitamin and mineral levels.**
- Vitamin B12 works in conjunction with folic acid and is essential for the production of genetic material called DNA. Vegans or those on a meat- and dairy-free diet are most at risk of being deficient in vitamin B12 and should consult their doctor. Meat, poultry, eggs, dairy products and fortified breakfast cereals are good sources of vitamin B12.
- Calcium, found in dairy products, nuts, bread and fish with edible bones like sardines, is vital for the formation of bones and teeth.
- Iron is crucial for both mother and baby (see page 23), and is responsible for the production of red blood cells. Iron is found mainly in meat, poultry, fish, eggs and leafy green vegetables.

- Vitamin C improves the absorption of iron and is found in citrus fruits, tomatoes, blackcurrants and potatoes.
- Vitamin D helps the body to absorb calcium and is therefore crucial in keeping bones healthy. Find it in margarine and oily fish, although sunlight is the best source of this nutrient.
- Zinc, found in meat, poultry, eggs and shellfish, also helps in the production of DNA, and may also help to improve fertility.
- Foods rich in manganese, such as oats, wheatgerm, chestnuts, rye bread and peas, promote the action of oestrogen in the baby.
- Vitamin B6, found in wholegrains and vegetables, aids oestrogen metabolism.

A varied, healthy diet should provide all the nutrients your body needs in amounts that can be readily absorbed. Although if you do choose to take a multi-vitamin and mineral supplement, opt for one that does not exceed 100 per cent of the RDA (recommended daily amount) of any of the nutrients.

If planning a baby, stop taking the contraceptive pill three months before you wish to conceive and use alternative methods instead. This allows your body to cleanse itself of synthetic hormones and establish its own cycle. These hormones can deplete your body of essential vitamins, such as folic acid, vitamins C and E and the mineral zinc, while iron and copper levels are raised.

**4 Eat three healthy meals a day** that are nutrient dense, rather than those laden with empty calories, such as cakes, sweets and fatty foods. Fats should make up no more than 30 per cent of your daily calorie intake. Choose foods that contain unsaturated or monounsaturated fats, rather than saturated fats which are found in cream, full-fat cheese, mayonnaise, butter, fatty meats and processed foods. Opt instead for olive oil, low-fat spreads, yogurt and low-fat fromage frais.

If you are very overweight prior to conceiving, diet in moderation and steer clear of faddy and extreme eating plans. Aim for 1,200–1,500 calories a day and a weight loss of no more than 500 g–1 kg (1–2 lb) a week. Maintain an optimum level of body fat – at least 18 per cent of body weight. If the level drops below this, hormone imbalances can occur, which may result in a failure to ovulate.

If you are very underweight, now is the time to make sure you eat regular meals based on the five main food groups, including plenty of fruits, vegetables and cereals to increase your fertility. Avoid a diet that is too full of refined and processed foods and make sure you have an adequate amount of fibre. See pages 18–23 for more information on healthy diets.

**5 Stop smoking.** Nicotine affects the production of female hormones and depletes fertility. If you stop smoking, your baby is less likely to have breathing and feeding problems, be born premature and underweight and be prone to infection. You will also reduce the risk of cot death and childhood cancer. (See page 28.)

**6 Cut down on alcohol and caffeine.** Heavy or frequent drinking reduces fertility as well as increasing the risk of miscarriage, and affects a baby's development during

pregnancy. In a small research study, women who were having problems conceiving reduced their alcohol intake to 5 units or less per week and their fertility rates significantly improved as a result.

Alcohol also influences the body's ability to absorb vital nutrients, such as B vitamins, iron and zinc. Health organizations differ in their advice; some believe drinking a maximum of 1–8 units of alcohol a week is perfectly safe, while others recommend cutting it out altogether. (See page 28). Avoid binge drinking and, if you feel unable to cut down, seek medical help and advice.

It is also important to reduce the amount of coffee you drink, since caffeine is a stimulant and has been linked to early miscarriage. Don't forget that tea, cocoa and fizzy drinks also contain caffeine. Try to drink 6–8 glasses of water a day, plus more natural fruit juices. (See page 29 for more details.)

**7 Cut out drugs.** Check with your doctor or health specialist about the suitability of any prescribed medications that you may be on, such as an asthma inhaler. This also includes over-the-counter remedies for minor ailments, aromatherapy oils, herbal remedies and slimming pills.

Street drugs, such as cannabis, have been linked to low sperm count in men and with premature birth, while ecstasy may cause cleft palates and heart problems. Cocaine increases the likelihood of abnormality, bleeding and premature birth. Heroin reduces fertility, trebles the risk of miscarriage or stillbirth and raises the risk of premature birth. For drug reduction and rehabilitation it is important to seek medical advice. (See page 29 for more details.)

**8 Double check** that your rubella (German measles) vaccination is up to date; a blood test will be able to check. If you need a booster, wait for three months for the vaccine virus to clear from your blood before you hope to conceive. This also applies if you have had vaccines to protect against tropical diseases when you are travelling abroad.

**9 Get fit.** A fit and healthy body will not only make you feel more energetic and supple, but will help you to relax. Furthermore, it will make it to easier to cope with your changing shape and labour. If you haven't exercised for a while, it is advisable to consult your doctor or health specialist before you begin. Walking, swimming and yoga keep you active and suit many levels of fitness, while a gym may be able to develop a special programme of exercise for you. Take things slowly, gradually building up an exercise programme that suits you.

**10 It is important** to follow food safety guidelines; (see pages 24–31 for more details).

## WHAT ABOUT YOUR MAN?

Just as diet and lifestyle affect a women's ability to conceive, so it can also play a part in a man's fertility levels. A sperm takes 72 days to produce so it is important for your partner to make changes to his lifestyle 2–6 months before conception. Alcohol, even in moderate amounts, can reduce the production of healthy sperm. Research has also shown that smoking can affect the quality of sperm – children born to fathers who smoke are at a much greater risk of childhood cancers and cot death. Illegal drugs, such as cocaine, are also known to affect sperm mobility.

Boost fertility levels by eating oily fish, such as fresh tuna, mackerel, herrings, sardines and salmon, which are rich in omega-3 fatty acids. Monounsaturated fats, including olive oil, and polyunsaturated fats, such as sunflower oil, also provide essential fatty acids. Try to eat foods rich in vitamins A, B, C and E and boost levels of zinc as part of a mixed vitamin supplement or take zinc on its own plus a daily 130 mcg supplement of selenium. Researchers have found that high levels of vitamin C may help the most common cause of male infertility – the clustering together or "aggulution" of sperm. Also lycopene, the natural chemical that gives tomatoes and red fruits their bright colour, can apparently boost the ability of sperm to swim. Seek medical advice before embarking on such a vitamin supplement programme.

# PREGNANCY

Discovering you are pregnant is exhilarating and exciting. You may want to shout the news from the rooftops, but now is the time to take things slowly, and to enjoy the next few months as you get used to the huge changes that are about to happen to your body and your life.

# what makes a healthy diet?

Although a healthy diet is important for the whole family at all times, it is especially important when you are pregnant. Your body must have the right fuel in order to function efficiently and cope with the demands of a growing baby inside you.

In order to help you visualize which foods you need and the proportions you need to eat them in for a nutritious and well-balanced diet, the five food groups have been divided into a simple pyramid shape for easy, at-a-glance reference.

# THE FOOD PYRAMID

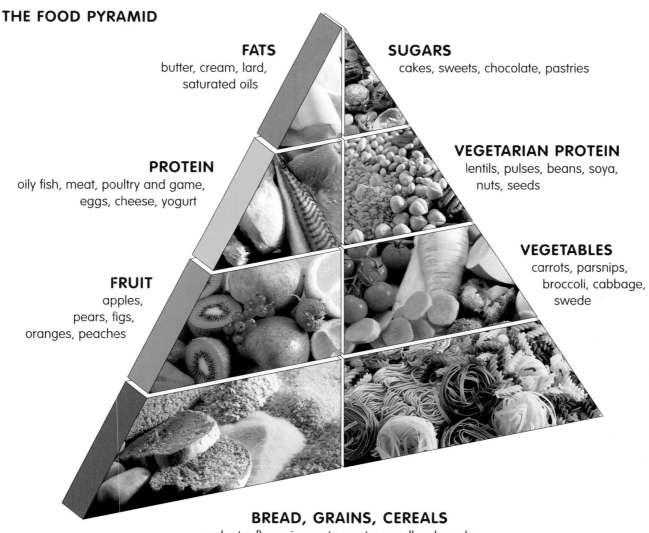

**FATS**
butter, cream, lard, saturated oils

**SUGARS**
cakes, sweets, chocolate, pastries

**PROTEIN**
oily fish, meat, poultry and game, eggs, cheese, yogurt

**VEGETARIAN PROTEIN**
lentils, pulses, beans, soya, nuts, seeds

**FRUIT**
apples, pears, figs, oranges, peaches

**VEGETABLES**
carrots, parsnips, broccoli, cabbage, swede

**BREAD, GRAINS, CEREALS**
polenta, flour, rice, oats, pasta, noodles, breads, potatoes, yams and plantain

The food groups that make up the layers of the pyramid, arranged in order of the volume which should be eaten are: **Bread, grains, cereals** – these should be eaten in the largest amounts; aim to eat a portion in each meal. **Fruit and vegetables** – very few of us eat enough from this layer; aim to eat five portions a day. **Proteins** – the amount of protein needed is often less than you think, although this needs to go up slightly when you are pregnant. Proteins provide a good source of calcium, vital for the growing child. At the top of the pyramid are the **Fats and sugars** – these should be kept as a treat and only eaten in moderation.

## BREAD, GRAINS AND CEREALS

Choose from bread, fortified low-sugar breakfast cereals, potatoes, plantains, yams, couscous, rice and pasta, plus wholegrains such as oats, barley and rye. This food group should be the main foundation of our diet, since it contains carbohydrates for energy, protein for growth and repair, and B vitamins for development. They're also low in fat, filling and economical to buy. Starchy foods, especially wholegrain breakfast cereals, wholemeal bread and brown rice also provide fibre, which prevents constipation, a common problem in pregnancy. Furthermore, starches and fibre are broken down more slowly, leaving you feeling full for longer. Healthy eating guidelines recommend that about half of our daily calorie intake should come from carbohydrate or starchy foods. **Aim for 5 servings a day.**

## FRUIT AND VEGETABLES

Fresh or frozen fruit and vegetables supply valuable vitamins, minerals and fibre. While it is important to avoid liver during pregnancy because of its high vitamin A content, the plant form of vitamin A, known as beta carotene, poses no risk. Found in brightly coloured fruits and vegetables, such as carrots, red peppers, mangoes, cantaloupe melons and also green leafy vegetables, beta carotene is an important antioxidant (see box on page 23), believed to help protect the body against some forms of cancer.

Green vegetables, such as spinach, kale, broccoli, watercress, Brussels sprouts and green beans, provide valuable folates (folic acid), which can help to reduce the risk of birth defects in the unborn child. (It is also recommended that you take a folic acid supplement; see page 11 for more details.) Green vegetables are also a good source of vitamin K, necessary for healthy blood clotting, as well as iron, which aids the formation of red blood cells.

The antioxidant vitamin C, found mainly in citrus fruits, kiwi fruit, peaches, berries, blackcurrants and tomatoes, is required by the body on a daily basis for growth and repair of body tissues, healthy skin and the healing of wounds. Yet most importantly for mums-to-be, the vitamin aids the absorption of calcium, vital for your baby's growing bones and teeth, as well as iron. Like folates, Vitamin C is an unstable nutrient and is lost through water, heating and oxidation, therefore it is important to eat fruits and vegetables raw whenever possible, and to steam rather than boil them.

**Aim for 5 or more servings a day.**

## FOODS RICH IN FOLATES

- Broccoli, Brussels sprouts, spinach and green beans, with smaller amounts in potatoes, cauliflower, frozen peas and cabbage
- Oranges, with smaller amounts in grapefruit and bananas
- Pulses
- Fortified breakfast cereals
- Fortified bread
- Yeast extract
- Milk
- Orange juice

## MEAT, FISH, EGGS AND NON-ANIMAL PROTEINS

These protein-rich foods are essential for the maintenance and repair of every cell in the body and the growth of new cells in your baby. Meat, fish and eggs are rich in iron and zincs along with vitamins A, D and B12, which works in conjunction with folic acid for a healthy nervous system. Oily fish is an excellent source of omega-3 fatty acids (see box opposite).

Proteins from plant sources, such as dried beans, lentils, seeds, tofu and nuts, do not contain all of the essential amino acids, unlike animal proteins. Yet nutritionists now suggest it is unnecessary for vegetarians to combine plant proteins in every meal to achieve the correct balance of amino acids, provided they eat a varied diet of dairy produce, nuts, pulses, eggs and vegetables on a daily basis.

**Aim to eat 2–3 servings a day.**

## DAIRY PRODUCE

Dairy products, such as milk, yogurt and cheese, are rich in protein, calcium and vitamins A and D, with small amounts of zinc and some B group vitamins. Although a pregnant woman's body becomes more efficient in absorbing calcium from foods, it is still important to include a variety of dairy products in your diet, especially towards the end of pregnancy – 200 ml (7 fl oz) of milk contains the same amount of calcium as a small pot of yogurt or about 40 g (1½ oz) hard cheese, 50 g (2 oz) cottage cheese and 100 g (3½ oz) fromage frais, and each is the equivalent of a single serving. If you dislike dairy foods or are following a vegan diet, then it is important to eat enriched soya milk, soya yogurts and tofu instead. Vitamin D helps the body to absorb calcium.

**Aim to eat 2–3 servings a day.**

## FATS AND SUGARS

Cakes, pastries and sweets are full of refined sugar and saturated fat, which provide plenty of calories, yet minimal nutrients. Ideally fats should provide no more than 30 per cent of the calories in your daily diet. Beware of hidden fats in processed foods and try to eat more mono-unsaturated fats, such as olive oil, and polyunsaturated fats, including sunflower oil, rather than saturated fats found in butter and margarine. Grilling, stir-frying and slow cooking require little or no extra oil; deep-fried foods, such as fish and chips, should be considered as a treat. While dieting is not advisable during pregnancy, eating large quantities of fats and sugars will pile on the weight, which may be difficult to lose after the birth. However, fats found in oily fish, rapeseed oil and soya bean oil contain beneficial fatty acids, vital for your baby's development (see box).

**Eat only occasionally.**

### WHY IS IRON SO IMPORTANT?

Iron combines with protein to form haemoglobin in red blood cells, and while pregnant your blood supply can increase by up to 30 per cent to meet the growing needs of your baby. Iron can be stored in the body, so if you were eating healthily before conception, your iron stores should be at an adequate level. While pregnant, the body is also able to absorb more iron from foods, especially from red meat. Vegetarians can boost iron absorption from plant sources, such as beans, lentils, eggs, nuts, breads, fortified breakfast cereals, pasta, spinach, watercress and dried fruit, by eating them with foods rich in vitamin C, like a glass of orange juice. Tea hinders absorption. However, some women do develop anaemia during pregnancy even after eating healthily, and may be prescribed an iron supplement by their doctor or hospital consultant.

### ANTIOXIDANTS

Antioxidant nutrients include vitamins A, C and E and minerals, such as selenium and zinc. These help to protect us against the damage caused by free radicals, which attack the genetic material held inside the body's cells, causing it to mutate. Antioxidants also stimulate the immune system and normalize the balance of hormone-like chemicals in the body that control pain, inflammation and fever. A diet that contains plenty of fresh fruits and vegetables, wholegrain cereals, seeds, pulses and moderate amounts of meat and fish will provide a good source of protective antioxidants.

### OMEGA-3 FATTY ACIDS

Omega-3 fatty acids, found in oily fish such as mackerel, herrings, salmon, sardines and fresh tuna, along with walnuts, soya beans and rapeseed oil, have been found to play a crucial role in the development of a baby's brain, nerves and eyes, as well as having a beneficial effect on birth weight and length of pregnancy. Studies on Eskimo women, who eat plenty of oily fish, found that they rarely gave birth prematurely.

# food safety in pregnancy

We are all susceptible to food poisoning bugs, but during pregnancy the immune system changes. In order to carry a baby, a women's body has to accept new genetic material from the father and not reject it, and it may be for this reason that pregnant women are more at risk. Furthermore, food poisoning can also put an unborn child at risk.

**"In the right conditions, one bacterium can multiply into one million in just over 3 hours!"**

The three most prominent food-related diseases are listed below. However, these are extremely rare and avoidable if you know which foods are safe to eat and which ones you should avoid. With a few simple precautions you should sail through pregnancy, happy and healthy.

## LISTERIOSIS

This is a rare flu-like illness, caused by the bacterium Listeria monocytogenes and although the symptoms may be mild in a mother, they can affect her developing baby, leading to miscarriage, stillbirth or severe illness.

### FOODS TO WATCH:

Avoid foods which may contain Listeria monocytogenes including:
- All soft, mould-ripened cheeses, even those made with pasteurized milk, such as Brie, Camembert, Cambozola, Chaumes, Lymes Wold, Pont L'Eveque and Tallegio.
- Blue-veined cheeses, such as Bavarian blue, blue Brie, blue Shropshire, Danish blue, Dolcelatte, Gorgonzola, Roquefort and Stilton.

- All meat, fish and vegetable pâtés, unless they are canned or UHT; also avoid anything made with liver.
- Some cook-chill meals (not frozen) – always check the use-by date and reheat thoroughly, especially ready-to-eat poultry. Always follow manufacturer's instructions and stir food well during cooking. Only reheat foods once.
- Ice cream from soft whip machines. (Wrapped or block ice creams are fine.)

Avoid soft mould-ripened cheeses.

## CHEESES THAT ARE SAFE TO EAT:

**Hard cheeses:**
Austrian smoked, Babybel, Caerphilly, Cheddar, Cheshire, Derby, Edam, Emmental, English goat's Cheddar, feta made with pasteurized milk, Gloucester, Gouda, Gruyère, halloumi, Jarlsberg, Lancashire, Leicester, mozzarella, paneer, Parmesan, pecorino (hard), provolone, Port Salut and Wensleydale.

**Soft cheeses:**
Cottage cheese, curd cheese, cream cheese, processed cheese spreads, fromage frais, mascarpone, Quark, ricotta (and yogurt).

There is no need to avoid:
cheeses, pâtés or cook-chill meals if you are not planning to have a baby, or once you have had your baby – even if you are intending to breastfeed.

## SALMONELLOSIS

This dangerous but rare condition is caused by the Salmonella bacteria and results in sickness, diarrhoea and dehydration. Mild Salmonella poisoning will not harm your baby directly, but severe cases could lead to miscarriage or early labour.

### FOODS TO WATCH:

- Avoid foods that contain raw or lightly cooked eggs, a common cause of food poisoning. These include homemade mayonnaise (bought mayonnaise uses pasteurized eggs which are safe), homemade ice cream or sorbets, mousses, uncooked cheesecakes and royal icing on Christmas and wedding cakes. Eat only hard-boiled eggs, well-cooked scrambled egg and poached or fried eggs, where both the white and yolk are set right through. Pasteurized dried egg whites or whole eggs can be bought in supermarkets and are ideal as an alternative to use for lightly cooked custards and royal icing instead of fresh eggs.
- Avoid unpasteurized milk and soft unpasteurized cows', goats' and sheeps' cheeses. Use only pasteurized, sterilized or UHT milk.
- Take care with raw or undercooked poultry and meat. Salmonella is destroyed by heat, so make sure meat and poultry are cooked thoroughly and at oven temperatures of 180°C (350°F), Gas Mark 4 or above. To test to see if poultry is cooked, pierce the flesh through the thickest part with a skewer or a fork – the juices should run clear, never pink or red. Keep raw and cooked meat separate to avoid cross contamination and wash your hands thoroughly after handling.

Caerphilly is delicious and safe to eat during pregnancy.

## TOXOPLASMOSIS

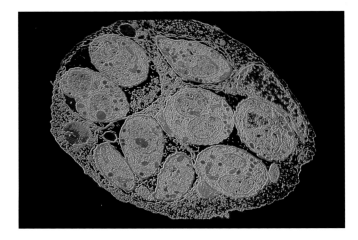

The Toxoplasmosis bacterium is dangerous to the unborn child.

This rare illness may cause blindness, brain damage, miscarriage or possible stillbirth and is caused by the parasite Toxoplasma gondii, which may be found in cat faeces and raw meat, although this bacterium can be killed in meat by thorough cooking.

### FOODS TO WATCH:
- Raw or undercooked meat and fish.
- Vegetables and salads, especially pre-washed varieties. Wash carefully at home to remove all traces of soil.
- Unpasteurized milk, including goats' and sheeps' milk.

## WHAT ABOUT SHELLFISH?
Since shellfish cause more bouts of food poisoning than any other food, it is important to take extra care when pregnant. Do not eat uncooked shellfish and only buy from a reputable fish shop or wet fish counter in a supermarket with a date stamp. Use on the day of purchase, store in the refrigerator and cook all shellfish thoroughly, including oysters. Be extra vigilant when preparing mussels. (Pink-coloured prawns, lobster and crab have already been cooked, but be sure to rinse prawns well under cold running water before use). Avoid raw fish dishes, such as sushi or uncooked marinated fish.

## CURED MEATS
Take extra care with cured meats, such as Parma ham, salami and chorizo sausage. Buy ready-wrapped meats and use well within the use-by date. The same applies to smoked salmon and other smoked fish and meats; it is wise to cook these before serving.

## BARBECUES
Be extra vigilant with barbecued meat, especially poultry, as it can look well-cooked on the outside but may still be pink in the middle. Follow the simple guidelines below, and if you are at all unsure, avoid altogether.
- Don't try to hurry a barbecue. Make sure the coals are white hot before you start cooking.
- Check meat carefully before eating to ensure it is thoroughly cooked through. Cut a slice off a piece of meat or halve a burger to make sure it is cooked in the centre. If it's still pink, put it back on the barbecue and

check again after 5–10 minutes, or longer if it is very underdone.

- Fish flesh should look opaque and flake easily when cooked. Take extra care with whole fish on the bone.

## EATING OUT

If you are unhappy about a meal that you have ordered, regardless of whether it's in an expensive restaurant or a budget-priced pub, have a quiet word with the waiter or manager as soon as you realize it is not quite cooked. Don't be tempted to eat it, rather than make a fuss.

## BUT IT'S NOT JUST FOOD...

If you have cats and kittens, Salmonella, Campylobacter and Toxoplasma may be present in their faeces. Get someone else in the family to clean cat litter trays and if that is impossible, make sure you wear gloves when handling them. Wash your gloved hands and then wash your hands. Soiled litter should be changed every day and the tray washed regularly, preferably by someone else. Do not allow cats to walk on work surfaces or anywhere near food preparation areas. Keep animal bowls, spoons, and can openers separate from human crockery and wash them with separate brushes. Always wash your hands before food preparation and after stroking your cat. Make sure children's garden sand pits are covered

when they are not in use and wear rubber gloves when gardening. Toxoplasma may be present in garden soil if it has been fouled by cats. Be sure to wash your hands thoroughly after gardening.

If you live on or near a farm, avoid contact with lambs and sheep that have just given birth or miscarried as they may carry Listeria, Chlamydia Psittaci or Toxoplasma, which could in extreme cases cause a miscarriage or harm your unborn child.

## GOOD NEWS

Not all bacteria are bad; some are actually good for us. It is now recognized that the "friendly" bacteria found in live yogurt discourage the harmful bacteria and yeasts in the gut that can lead to stomach upsets and can also reduce bad breath associated with digestive disorders. Live yogurt can also restore vital intestinal bacteria destroyed after a course of antibiotics and is a useful treatment for thrush when used externally. Look for "live" yogurt as well as those labelled "bio", which contain various types of beneficial bacteria.

## THE BODY'S PROTECTION

The placenta acts as a filter and is able to keep most bacteria, some drugs and harmful substances from reaching the baby. Viruses or germs are smaller than bacteria and can slip through the placenta and therefore it is wise to be cautious about potential food risks.

---

### FOODS TO AVOID AT-A-GLANCE

- soft, mould-ripened and blue cheeses
- unpasteurized milk
- raw and lightly cooked eggs
- liver and foods containing liver (see page 30)
- undercooked meat and poultry
- peanuts and peanut products, if there is a history of food allergy, asthma or eczema in yourself, your partner or any other existing children.

# what else to avoid?

## SMOKING

It is well documented that smoking affects the short- and long-term health of your baby. When you smoke, carbon monoxide and nicotine pass into your bloodstream and as a result your baby gets less oxygen, plus the heart rate increases. Your baby may also be smaller and born premature. Babies born to parents who both smoke are more prone to breathing difficulties, nose and throat infections, and asthma while babies born to non-smoking mothers with partners who smoke are also at risk. They are more likely to be smaller and have a greater risk of health problems in childhood.

If you are trying for a baby, what better reason or time to give up smoking – it not only harms your baby but reduces your fertility too.

Even if you find you are pregnant unexpectedly, try to give up smoking as soon as you can, and ask your doctor or health practitioner for advice.

After the birth, don't be tempted to slip back into old ways. Nicotine is transferred to your baby through breastfeeding. Encourage your partner and visitors to smoke in another room or outside so that your baby doesn't passive smoke – not only is this dangerous, it may also increase the risk of cot death.

## ALCOHOL

Current health guidelines vary in their recommendations on alcohol consumption. Some recommend that pregnant women drink no more than 1–2 units a day, with a maximum of 8 units a week. Others suggest avoiding alcohol altogether. While there is no evidence to suggest that light or occasional drinking (no more than 2 units a day) will harm your baby, heavy or frequent drinking can

cause serious developmental problems. Talk it over with your partner, or health specialist. You may prefer to reduce or cut out alcohol altogether while you are trying for a baby, gradually introducing the odd social drink again once your pregnancy is well established.

## DRUGS

Illegal drugs, including heroin, cocaine, ecstasy, cannabis and amphetamines can put your baby at serious risk (see page 14). Even some over-the-counter medicines can harm your baby, so always consult your midwife or health practitioner, and remind her of any regular medicines you may have been taking prior to conceiving.

Avoid taking multi-vitamin supplements that provide more than 100 per cent of the RDA (recommended daily allowance). Cod liver oil capsules contain retinol, the animal form of vitamin A, and it is important not to take more than 3,000 mcg per day. Most cod liver oil supplements contain about a quarter of this level and so are considered a safe and important source of omega-3 fatty acids (see page 23). Most vitamin supplements contain vitamin A in the form of beta carotene, not retinol, but it is worth checking. You can also buy vitamin and mineral supplements that have been specifically formulated for pregnant women. Be wary of herbal and homeopathic remedies and check with your health practitioner or homeopath before taking these.

## CAFFEINE

Caffeine, found mainly in coffee, but also in tea, chocolate, cola and in some "high-energy" drinks, is a stimulant and diuretic, so increases the excretion of calcium. Current research suggests that excess coffee consumption (more than 300 mg of caffeine per day,

which is equivalent to four cups of instant coffee) can slightly increase the risk of miscarriage in early pregnancy. Until more research is carried out, it is probably wise to cut down your coffee intake while pregnant and breastfeeding to a single cup of ground coffee or 2 cups of instant coffee a day. However as many women find that they go off tea and coffee while they are pregnant you may have already cut down on your caffeine intake.

**CAFFEINE CONTENT OF DRINKS PER 150 ML (¼ PINT) CUP:**

| | | |
|---|---:|---|
| Ground coffee | 115 | mg |
| Instant coffee | 65 | mg |
| Tea | 40 | mg |
| Cola | 18 | mg |
| Cocoa | 4 | mg |
| Drinking chocolate | 3 | mg |
| Decaffeinated coffee | 3 | mg |
| (or a 125 g (4 oz) bar of plain chocolate | 80 | mg) |

## HERBAL TEA

Some herbal teas or infusions may help to relieve minor problems related to pregnancy. For example, ginger tea calms morning sickness, camomile aids digestion, and peppermint relieves wind and soothes stomach acids. Plus, they make a good caffeine-free alternative to tea and coffee. Any product bought as a "tea bag" type infusion from a supermarket or health food shop can be considered safe but don't make teas from loose herbs that you have bought or grown yourself. Raspberry leaf tea is often used during pregnancy because of its oxytocic properties (it helps to strengthen uterine contractions). It is therefore important not to use this product until the later stages of pregnancy, from about 36 weeks.

If in any doubt about a herbal tea, consult your health practitioner or homeopath first.

## LIVER

Liver is considered unsuitable for pregnant women or those hoping to conceive as it contains high levels of retinol, a substance converted by the body into vitamin A. High levels of retinol in the body have been linked to birth defects.

Although retinol-related birth defects are extremely rare, it is advisable to avoid liver and foods containing liver, such as liver sausage and pâté. Just an acorn-sized piece of calf's liver is enough to supply an adult's daily requirement of vitamin A. Retinol is fat soluble and it is not easily broken down by the body and this is why excessive amounts of the vitamin can pose a problem in pregnant women.

## PEANUTS

Only women who have a history of food allergy, asthma or eczema in themselves, their partners or in any existing children should avoid eating peanuts, or products containing peanuts during pregnancy or breastfeeding. Consult your midwife or health practitioner if you have any concerns.

## OTHER FOODS TO WATCH:
- peanut butter
- unrefined groundnut oil
- some bought cakes, biscuits and pastries
- some ice creams
- some cereal bars and confectionery
- satay sauce and some curries

Check with your doctor as some eczema creams also contain peanut oil.

## WHAT ABOUT FOOD ADDITIVES?
If these weren't a problem before you conceived, then they should not become a problem during pregnancy. In general, food additives are considered safe, but it is wise to try and cut down the amount of highly processed foods you eat as a matter of course.

## ARE PESTICIDES DANGEROUS?
Just as nutrients can be passed on to your unborn baby, so can artificial pesticide residues; this also applies when breastfeeding. Buying organic foods can be costly and unless foods are bought from a reputable retailer may not always be what is claimed on the label. But it is worth making the change, if you can, as babies are more vulnerable during pregnancy and during their first year. The amount of food that a baby eats is high in relation to its size and their liver is unable to deal with toxic substances in the same way that an adult's can.

> **"If you're not sure about a certain food, play safe and don't eat it!"**

# how safe is your kitchen?

Hygiene in the kitchen is always important but it is even more so when you are pregnant. Most of the following suggestions are common sense, but it is worth reminding the rest of the family about some of the basic do's and don'ts of food safety.

## BEFORE YOU BEGIN

✓ wash your hands after handling pets, gardening and before you begin any kind of food preparation.

✓ always wash salad leaves, even if the label says pre-washed; scrub vegetables and rinse rice and dried pulses before use.

✓ use separate chopping boards for raw and cooked meats; use separate knives for cooked and uncooked meat; and use separate cutlery and bowls for pets.

✓ change dishcloths and tea towels frequently.

✓ store eggs away from other foods. Wash your hands after handling the shells. Cooking will kill any germs present, but bacteria is also present on the outside of the egg too.

## WHEN COOKING

✓ make sure that food is always reheated thoroughly to at least 70°C (158°F) for a minimum of 2 minutes.

✓ stir foods to make sure they are evenly heated, especially when using a microwave.

✓ serve foods as soon as they are ready.

✓ keep to manufacturers' recommended timings on packaged food.

✓ If you are making food in advance, cover it after cooking and allow it to cool at room temperature. Once it is cool enough, preferably within 2 hours, transfer it to the refrigerator and keep it chilled until use.

## WHAT ABOUT LEFTOVERS?

✓ keep foods covered.

✓ transfer foods to the refrigerator as soon as they are cool enough.

✗ don't reheat cooked foods more than once.

✗ don't refreeze defrosted frozen raw foods unless they have been cooked thoroughly. Then allow to cool at room temperature. Freeze straight away once cooled.

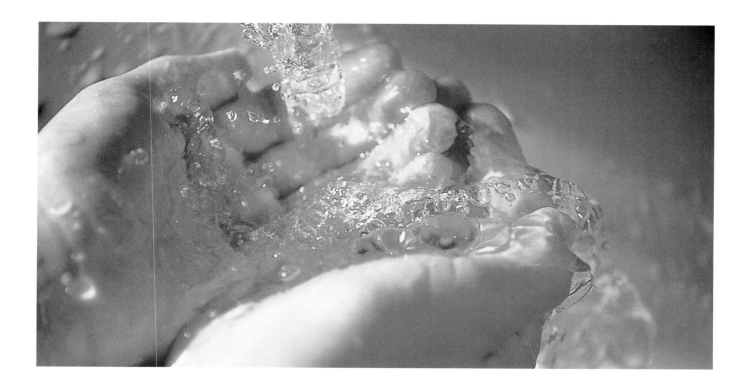

## IN THE REFRIGERATOR

✓ check "use by" and "best before" dates on food and drink labels and consume items before their 'best before dates'.

✓ make sure the coldest part of the refrigerator is no more than 5°C (41°F).

✓ stand defrosting foods on a large plate or tray to catch any drips.

✓ make sure raw meat and poultry are kept away from cooked foods. Keep all foods well covered, and store raw meat towards the bottom of the refrigerator.

✗ don't open the refrigerator door unnecessarily. It takes 30 minutes for the refrigerator to return to the preset temperature once the door has been opened.

## IN THE FREEZER

✓ check the temperature of the freezer, it should be -18°C (0°F) or lower. Buy a freezer thermometer if necessary.

✓ rotate foods, so that you use older foods first.

✓ if you have young children, buy a childproof door lock so they won't be tempted to open the freezer door and leave it ajar.

✓ defrost a chest freezer once or twice a year and an upright one, three or four times a year.

✓ get frozen food into the freezer as quickly as possible after your shopping trip. Ideally take an insulated cool bag with you, especially during the summer.

✗ don't freeze any more than 10 per cent of your freezer's capacity in new unfrozen foods in any 24 hours, unless the freezer has been set to fast freeze.

✗ never defrost foods in hot water or leave in a warm place. Although bacteria cannot multiply in frozen food, they can soon increase as the temperature rises. Defrost food in the refrigerator.

✗ never cook food that has not completely defrosted. Use a knife or skewer to check it has defrosted right through.

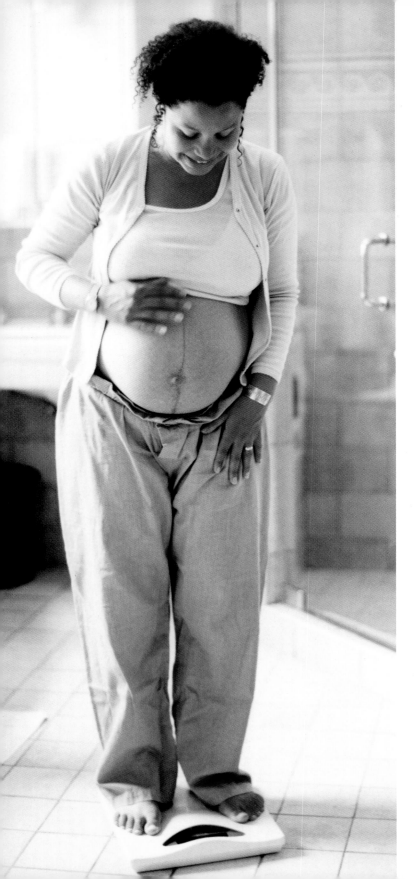

# your changing shape

Your body will change shape quite dramatically during the nine months of pregnancy. This can be a liberating and exhilarating experience for some women, who literally seem to blossom and glow, while others need time to adjust to their new shape.

## WEIGHT GAIN

Weight gain can vary from one pregnant woman to another, as can the shape of the growing "bump". Some women seem to gain weight almost immediately, while others seem to conceal their changing shape for longer. While you expect to see a growing waistline, plumper arms, thighs, hips and breasts may come as bit of a surprise, particularly in the early stages of pregnancy, but it is important to go with the changes and enjoy them, rather than become obsessive about dieting and weight loss at this time.

Antenatal weight gain will vary according to pre-pregnancy weight. For example, overweight women should gain less than normal weight women, while underweight women should gain more.

---

**RECOMMENDED WEIGHT GAIN:**
- Overweight women 5 kg (14 lb/1 stone)
- Normal weight women 12 kg (28 lb/2 stones)
- Underweight women 18 kg (42 lb/3 stones)

LEFT  With your first child you will probably experience movement from about 18 weeks. By about 20 weeks you should start to feel a bit more relaxed and will start to bloom.

BELOW  At 36 weeks the end is in sight, delivery at any time after 37 weeks is considered quite normal and by 40 weeks the baby is properly equipped to enter the world.

However, these recommended weight gains should only be used as a guide, since these figures were derived from average antenatal weight gains for a large number of women. So, if you are not following this pattern and your midwife or health practitioner is happy with your progress, there is nothing to worry about.

If you eat a varied and healthy diet and keep fatty foods, sweets and chocolates as an occasional treat, then you should not gain more weight than normal. It is also important to keep active; walking, swimming and yoga are ideal forms of gentle exercise.

Towards the end of pregnancy, you may feel uncomfortable after eating large meals. Try to eat small, frequent meals instead to keep energy levels up.

## SHOULD I EAT MORE?

During pregnancy, a woman's body becomes more efficient at utilizing energy and nutrients from the diet. While extra calories are required, the amount is surprisingly low – just 200 extra calories a day for the last trimester of pregnancy. That is equivalent to a jacket potato topped with 25 g (1 oz) of grated cheese or 2 slices of wholemeal toast spread with margarine or butter.

As a guide, let your appetite lead the way and eat when you feel hungry. Aim to eat a varied and healthy diet with plenty of fruits, vegetables and carbohydrates. Carbohydrates are broken down slowly by the body to give a gradual release of energy, rather than a surge as in the case of of sugary foods, which is followed by a sudden drop when that energy is used up.

## MORNING SICKNESS

Nausea, otherwise known as morning sickness, is very common in the early stages of pregnancy. It can occur from six weeks into a pregnancy and, unlike its name suggests, may not just happen in the morning but at any time of the day and evening. The reasons for sickness are largely unknown but hormonal changes are most likely to be the cause. It can be triggered by certain tastes, such as coffee, fried or spicy foods; strong smells, like perfume, petrol or cigarette smoke; and even stress. It very often begins with an odd taste in the mouth and feeling faint. Fortunately, the symptoms usually fade between 12–14 weeks, but some women may experience feelings of sickness right through their pregnancy. If the sickness is excessive or shows no sign of stopping, consult your midwife or health practitioner.

### HOW TO COPE:

• keep plain crackers or biscuits or dry cereal by your bed and eat a little before you get out of bed in the morning.

• try not to skip breakfast, even if you don't really feel like it. Choose something bland and starchy, such as a piece of toast or a currant bun.

• eat little and often; try five or six small meals instead of three larger ones and try to eat before you feel very hungry.

• if you feel your stomach can't cope with a proper meal, try soup (see pages 76–83) or a fruit smoothie (see page 65)

• avoid greasy or fried foods as these take a long time to digest.

• if the smell of cooking makes you feel nauseous, then ask your partner to take over or try eating more salads, sandwiches or quick-to-prepare meals.

• cut down, or cut out, tea and coffee; some women find sparkling mineral water helps.

• tiredness may also add to the nausea. Try to sit or lie down at least once a day.

• small quantities of ginger tea, ginger beer, crystallized stem ginger or a ginger biscuit may help.

• some studies have found that eating more foods rich in vitamin B6 may help. Try sesame seeds, raisins, bananas, baked potatoes or tuna fish.

• homeopathic remedies can help but consult a homeopath first.

• some women find that travel or sea sickness bands or bracelets can bring relief.

• don't be tempted to take any medication unless prescribed by your doctor or health practitioner.

## FOOD CRAVINGS

Many doctors regard food cravings as a myth, but myth or not, there is no reason why the sudden need for a certain food need not be indulged, as long as it's not too extreme or at the expense of eating a healthy and varied diet. Eating coal, soap, sand or mud are certainly some of the more extreme kinds of cravings (known as 'pica') and best resisted.

The sudden desire for chocolate or fruit may be in response to a drop in blood sugar levels in the body. But remember, chocolate will pile on the calories, so try not to indulge in sweet, sugary things too often. Some mums have found that a craving for olives or avocados has led to their baby also enjoying these foods once born.

### HOW TO COPE:
- have the occasional chocolate bar if desired.
- don't miss meals, even if you are feeling tired or sick, just reduce the amount you eat and try to eat at regular intervals.
- talk to your doctor or health practitioner if the urge to eat coal or other non-food stuffs changes to an actuality!

## CONSTIPATION

This common problem can be very uncomfortable and is caused by a combination of the hormone progesterone relaxing the smooth muscles lining the bowl, reducing bowel activity, along with the growing womb pressing against the intestines, so impeding bowel movements.

### HOW TO COPE:

- eat more fresh fruits, vegetables, high-fibre breads, cereals and other whole grains.
- try snacking on ready-to-eat dried figs, apricots, prunes or raisins.
- drink more liquids; you should aim to drink 6–8 glasses of water each day.
- some gentle exercise, such as walking or swimming, may help.
- do not take over-the-counter laxatives unless your doctor or health practitioner advises.

## INDIGESTION AND HEARTBURN

These are common symptoms of pregnancy partly caused by hormonal changes but also by pressure from your growing baby in the uterus towards the end of pregnancy. These symptoms are also more common in multiple pregnancies.

### HOW TO COPE:

- eat little and often throughout the day.
- try to eat meals slowly and avoid gulping your food.
- stop eating when you feel full, even if the portion isn't terribly large.
- cut down on spicy, acidic and fatty foods as these take longer to digest.
- bake, grill or steam foods, instead of frying.
- avoid orange or grapefruit juice.
- drink plain water, apple or cranberry juice; drink little and often.
- milk can also help as it neutralizes the acids in the stomach.
- cut down, or cut out, fizzy drinks, chocolate, coffee and other drinks containing caffeine.
- try peppermint or camomile tea.
- keep your head higher than your stomach when lying down.
- eat at least two hours before you go to bed.
- if the heartburn coincides with taking iron supplements, then stop them and see if the symptoms disappear; if they do then consult your doctor.

# getting ready for the birth

If you've just started maternity leave, now is the time to enjoy those tranquil few weeks before your baby arrives. Pamper yourself, have a hair cut, enjoy having lunch with friends and put your feet up when you can. Take a nap during the day, since your growing baby can make it difficult to sleep comfortably at night. You may also feel uncomfortable after eating large meals, so try smaller, more frequent, snack-sized meals and relax afterwards.

Many women have an urge to "nest" around this time, but this is perfectly normal, and getting ready for the arrival of your baby can be satisfying and rewarding, even sorting out cupboards takes on a new dimension.

As you may not feel up to long walks or anything too energetic, now is a good time to look at what is in your kitchen. Having a new baby completely changes your life, just a trip to the local shops can feel like a military exercise, so knowing the kitchen cupboards and freezer are well stocked is just one less thing to worry about.

When you cook, double favourite recipes and freeze half. This doesn't take much longer and if your partner isn't very keen on cooking it can be a boon. Label each dish with defrosting and reheating instructions. See opposite for ideas on filling the freezer.

I re-covered a chair just before my daughter was born and learned from experience. It would have been much more helpful to have had a freezer full of shepherd's pies! The following suggestions will help you to plan ahead. For other ideas see "Make now, eat later", pages 106–119.

- canned fish – tuna or salmon can be turned into a quick, tasty sandwich filling, pasta dish or fishcakes mixed with leftover mashed potato, a few frozen vegetables and a little lemon juice.

- canned beans – baked beans on toast sprinkled with grated cheese is a tasty, economical and satisfying lunch, while red kidney, haricot or cannellini beans make a high-fibre addition to soups, casseroles and filling salads.

- canned tomatoes – no kitchen can survive without these. They are ideal for quick pasta sauces, soups and casseroles. Passata or tetra packs of creamed tomatoes are excellent alternatives to canned tomatoes.

- dried pasta – a great base for a quick supper dish, mixed with a little fried bacon and a few mushrooms, pesto and cream or combined with mince or lentils. Cook extra and use the remainder in a pasta salad with pesto dressing.

- rice – long-grain or risotto, basmati or easy-cook brown rice, this versatile grain is suited to kedgeree, Indian-style pilau or biryani, or creamy Italian risotto.

- couscous – much quicker to prepare than potatoes, with no fiddly peeling required, couscous simply requires soaking in boiling water. Add lemon juice, olive oil and whatever flavourings you have to hand, such as chopped herbs, dried fruits, tomatoes, sweetcorn or green beans, for a tasty side dish or base for a salad.

- lentils – these don't need soaking and can simply be simmered in stock or water. Enliven red lentils with Indian spices for a tasty dhal, add green lentils to vegetable soups, or toss Puy lentils and roasted Mediterranean vegetables in balsamic vinegar for a filling supper dish.

- canned fruit – choose fruit in natural juice and serve with natural yogurt or fromage frais, or purée and stir into Greek yogurt, or top with a quick mix sponge for a speedy pud.

- longlife milk – with a new baby in the house, it's easy to run out of milk as you offer endless cups of tea to your excited visitors. Keep a couple of packs of longlife milk for emergencies. It's ideal for macaroni cheese, custard and quiches, too.
- frozen vegetables – these make a handy standby and are just as nutritious as fresh. Best buys are peas, sweetcorn, green beans, broad beans and bags of mixed vegetables.
- frozen fruit – bags of mixed berry fruits make a great vitamin-packed pudding. Simply cook in a little water with sugar and serve with Greek yogurt or use in trifles, fruit fools or as a base for crumbles.
- frozen fish – fish fillets can be poached from frozen for a low-fat, protein-packed supper and are often more nutritious than fresh, since they are frozen immediately. Cod, haddock, kippers and prawns make good standbys.

- homemade meals – it is worthwhile making a few meals prior to the birth and freezing them for later use when you are short of time or too tired to cook. Pasta sauces, fish pie, lasagne or casseroles can be the ideal pick-me-up. Homemade soup, frozen in individual portions, also makes a convenient and healthy lunch with just the addition of a slice of bread.
- homemade crumble topping – use while still frozen and since it stays free flowing, it's easy to remove the amount you need and sprinkle over fruit before baking.
- bread – keep a sliced granary or wholemeal loaf, pitta breads, Italian or Indian breads and ready-bake rolls.
- extras – butter, ice cream, ready-made puddings and even fishfingers can be a lifesaver. Large, ready-made Yorkshire puddings can be filled with sausages and vegetables, while sheets of puff or shortcrust pastry can be transformed into sweet or savoury pies.

# AFTER THE BIRTH

Nothing can prepare you for the impact of a new baby. It's exhilarating, exhausting, and physically demanding. Over the next few pages you will find tips on feeding your baby, getting your shape back after the birth and coping with overwhelming feelings of tiredness.

# being flexible

Having a new baby completely changes your life but it is also one of the most rewarding and thrilling times. Accept that it will take time to establish any routine in the early days and try not to be hard on yourself if things don't run as smoothly as you had hoped. The first few weeks will fly by in an endless blur of feeding, changing and sleeping. Even getting dressed and fitting in a meal can seem tricky some days. Just after my first daughter was born, I felt I was doing well if I was dressed before 11.30 am! But things will settle down and you will slip into a routine.

The key to coping and enjoying your baby is to be flexible. However capable you usually are, now is the time to accept all offers of help, from cooking and cleaning to walking the baby up the road. Take a nap yourself while the baby is asleep, and it may be useful to stick a note to the front door explaining that visitors are welcome, but not until after you have had your sleep.

Eat when you are hungry and when the baby is happy and does not require any attention, even if it is rather a strange time of the day. Somehow sleeping babies always have a knack of waking for a feed, just as you sit down to a meal yourself.

Even if you're feeling fit, don't be tempted to do too much. Many women feel so euphoric that they could move a mountain just after giving birth, but by the time their milk comes in on day three, they may feel quite weepy and tired. Although it's lovely to have visitors, allow yourself the odd day off.

The blurry first few days quickly fade and a pattern of feeding will begin to emerge and a new rhythm of life will unfold, but allow yourself as much time as you need – weeks, even months.

## LEARNING TO ADJUST

Giving birth is physically and emotionally demanding, so make sure that you give yourself enough time to recover.

Your body will go through huge physical and hormonal changes so don't be surprised if you feel on top of the world one minute and weepy the next minute.

Most mums will feel overwhelmed and have moments when they feel unable to cope. Don't panic, this is completely normal. If these feelings don't go away then ask your medical advisor for advice; you may be suffering from post-natal depression. If you are breastfeeding, things should be a little easier by week two. If not, speak to your medical advisor; however it can take up to eight weeks to really get established.

# feeding your baby

## BREASTFEEDING

It's widely acknowledged by health professionals, even by baby milk manufacturers, that breast is best. If you are not convinced that breastfeeding is for you, try it for the first few days or preferably weeks of your baby's life. Breastfeeding gives your baby the best possible start in life but it is a new skill that has to be learned by both you and your baby and it doesn't suit everyone.

Breastmilk contains all the nutrients your baby needs in the right proportions, along with antibodies which protect against infection, and high levels of fatty acids that promote brain and nervous tissue development. Furthermore, breastmilk is sterile, free, always at the right temperature, easily digestible, readily available and has the amazing ability to alter to meet the needs of a premature and growing baby.

The milk produced in the first few days after birth is known as colostrum, which contains antibodies to prevent infection. Sometimes referred to as "nature's vaccine", the rich and creamy colostrum also helps a new baby cope with small amounts of liquid as his kidneys adjust to independent life.

After about three days, your breasts may become large and heavy, which is a sign that they have begun to produce milk. Each feed is made up of thirst-quenching, fast-flowing fore milk, followed by the richer, more calorific hind milk to satisfy hunger. It is important to feed for at least 10–15 minutes on each breast to ensure your baby gets both types of milk. As your baby feeds, he stimulates the amount of milk you produce and it is this mechanism that will gradually increase your supply to match your baby's needs. You may find in the first few weeks or months that milk leaks from your nipples and it may be necessary to wear protective breast pads.

If you are planning to return to work in the next few months or want your partner to take care of some feeds, you can express milk. You can do this by hand or there are various types of breast pumps to choose from. Consult your breastfeeding counsellor for advice. Store expressed milk in a sterilized bottle in the refrigerator or freeze it if you want to keep it for longer than 24 hours.

Breastfeeding, like any new skill, can be difficult to master but give yourself time and don't feel rushed when feeding. If you have a young toddler, this can be tricky, but try to use it as a time to read to your child and a moment to put your feet up. If you have any problems or queries, don't be afraid or embarrassed to ask your health practitioner, midwife or breastfeeding counsellor for advice and guidance. While breastfeeding has many advantages, it is not for everyone. If for whatever reason you decide to bottle feed, don't feel guilty. Bottle feeding has its advantages too.

It is important to eat a varied, healthy diet and regular meals when breastfeeding. You'll probably find your appetite will increase as your body produces more milk, but try not to use it as an excuse to overindulge in sweets and cakes. By the same token, now is not the time to diet.

Foods that were a high risk during pregnancy are now no longer a problem, but if there is a history of peanut allergies within the immediate family, avoid eating nuts or foods containing traces of nuts. Some mothers believe that certain foods can upset a baby's stomach, including milk, orange juice, chillies, garlic, onions, beans and pulses, but there is little evidence to back this up and it is important to consult a health practitioner first before cutting foods out of your diet. The key to a healthy diet and good supply of milk is to eat foods from the five main food groups. (See pages 18–23 for more information.) Try to drink plenty of water too (6–8 glasses a day) and take as much rest as you can, especially in the early weeks. Try to avoid excessive amounts of caffeine as this passes into breastmilk and can cause abnormal activity and sleeplessness in your baby, as they have a lower ability to metabolize caffeine.

While the occasional glass of wine is not a problem as your body is able to metabolize this, alcohol in excessive amounts passes into breastmilk and can alter its taste, leaving your baby temporarily uncomfortable and irritable. Heavy smoking can decrease milk supply and can cause nausea and vomiting in your baby. Inhaling cigarette smoke increases a baby's risk of chest infections and puts him at a greater risk of sudden cot death.

**BREASTFEEDING TIPS**
- drink plenty of water and keep a glass of water by you when feeding.
- eat regularly, don't try to diet until you stop feeding. Snack on fruit, such as bananas and apples, rather than biscuits.
- give yourself time, feeding can't be hurried.
- breastfeeding helps to get your shape back more quickly.
- don't be afraid to ask for help if you are experiencing difficulties, even second or third time mums need help too.

## BOTTLE-FEEDING

Some women find that breastfeeding just isn't for them or their baby for whatever reason. You may feel disappointed, but don't let social pressures make you feel guilty. Bottle-feeding still enables you to build a close bond with your baby and it has many advantages over breastfeeding; it allows your partner to become involved with feeding and it is helpful if you are going back to work soon after the birth.

### FORMULA MILK

Baby milk or infant formula is most often sold in powdered form to be made up at home with boiled, cooled water. It is also available ready-made in cartons, which are slightly more expensive but are convenient when you are out. Manufacturers have tried to mimic breastmilk as closely as they can, adding important fatty acids and lactose (sugar), plus essential vitamins and minerals. Infant formula is available in two forms, whey-based formula for newborns and follow-on milk, with a higher proportion of milk protein (casein) to whey, plus higher levels of iron and vitamin D, for hungrier babies over six months old.

Soya-based infant formula and goats' milk infant formula are also available. Consult your doctor or health professional before opting for the latter. Cows' milk is not suitable as a drink for babies under 12 months, although it can be used in limited amounts in cooking from six months onwards.

### WHAT ABOUT OTHER DRINKS?

From about six weeks babies fed on formula milk can start to take cooled, boiled water. Don't be tempted to add flavourings or sweeteners, as a thirsty infant will happily drink water. Just as when you make up formula feeds, use freshly drawn and boiled water, rather than water that has been repeatedly boiled.

Breast fed babies of less than three to four months do not need drinks other than breastmilk, even in hot weather, as breastmilk adapts naturally to become more thirst-quenching when required.

### WHY NOT COWS' MILK?

Do not be tempted to feed your baby cows' milk. Although it is a good source of energy, protein, vitamins and minerals it is low in iron which is essential for a new born baby. Both formula milk and breastmilk contain iron and your baby will need this for his development for the first twelve months. Cows' milk can gradually be added to cooked food when your child is about six months old.

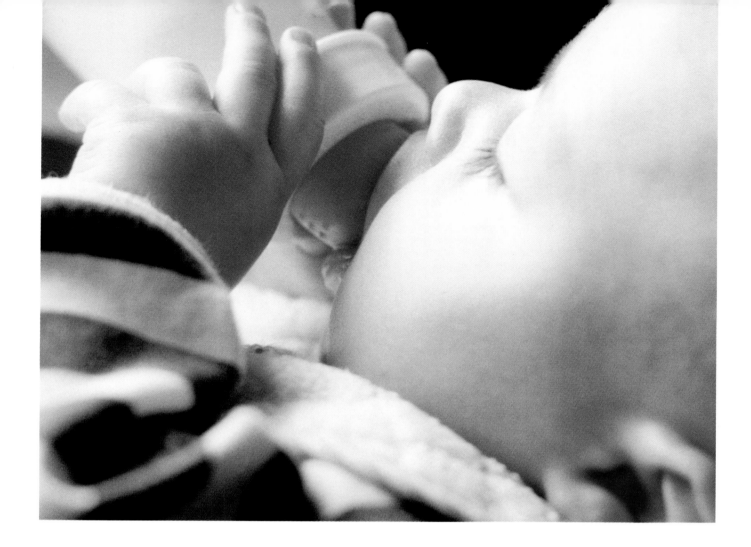

## TIPS FOR BOTTLE-FEEDING

- wash your hands thoroughly before preparing formula milk.
- sterilize bottles and teats until your baby is twelve months old.
- always follow the manufacturer's directions on the pack. Do not use more formula than recommended.
- use freshly drawn cold water that has only been boiled once.
- even bottled water will need to be boiled until your baby is six months old. Do not use bottled waters with a high mineral content, usually labelled "natural mineral water" or sparkling water, and do not use water from a tap fitted with a water softener. If you use a filter make sure it is changed regularly.
- keep bottles in the refrigerator until required or in an insulated bottle bag when you are out.
- do not reuse leftover formula.
- Babies vary in how often they want to feed. Bottle-fed babies tend to feed every 3-4 hours but may take a little time to settle into a routine.

# getting your shape back

While strict dieting is not advisable after giving birth, watching the type of foods you eat is important, as is gentle exercise. Weight loss post-pregnancy varies considerably from woman to woman and a lot will depend on your pre-pregnancy shape, your level of fitness and your age.

Two advantages of breastfeeding are that it uses up more calories than bottle-feeding and it makes your womb contract, helping to flatten your tummy.

It is important to start introducing gentle exercises after the birth. Start with gentle pelvic exercises such as Pelvic Tilting, which should be performed daily, several times throughout the day. Pelvic Tilts are easy to do and you can do them anywhere. Four weeks after the birth, you can move into doing main exercises such as Curl-downs and Small Hip Rolls if you have no apparent physical problems. Small Hip Rolls and Curl-downs should not however be performed immediately after the birth.

### Pelvic Tilting (suitable for straight after birth)
**1a** Lie on your back with knees bent and hip-width apart and feet flat on the floor. Push the lower back into the floor and tighten the abdominals.

**1b** Squeeze and lift the buttock muscles, tilting the pelvis upwards. Hold for a count of five. Release back down to the starting position. Repeat the exercise eight times.

### Curl-downs (suitable for four weeks after birth)
**2a** Sit with knees bent and feet hip-width apart. Turn the toes in slightly and hold your arms out-stretched in front of you. Slowly lower your back towards the floor, exhaling as you go. Be careful not to over-stretch.

**2b** Keeping the chin on the chest and the shoulders relaxed, squeeze your abdominals as you push yourself back up to the starting position. Repeat this eight times.

### Small Hip Rolls (suitable for four weeks after birth)
**3a** Lie on your back on a mat or towel with knees bent and feet together. Place your hands behind your head, elbows out. Breathe in and draw up your pelvic floor muscles. Hold for a count of two and then release. As you release, push very gently so that the vagina opens slightly. While you are doing this squeeze your abdominal muscles.

**3b** As you breathe out, let your knees drop over half-way to the right. Hold them in this position and breathe in. Breathe out and bring the legs back to the centre. Repeat to the left side, then repeat each side three times.

1a

1b

2a

2b

3a

3b

# coping with tiredness

Many new mums cannot believe how such a tiny bundle of joy can be quite so time consuming and exhausting, and are quite unprepared for the tiredness. Even if you feel fit and well straight after the birth, try not to overdo things. It can take six to twelve months to fully recover, both emotionally and physically, even after a straightforward birth. If you have had a caesarean or a difficult labour, you may feel quite battered and bruised.

When you're tired or feeling lonely, even the smallest of things can seem of major importance. If you've been working up to the birth of your baby, you will probably not have had the opportunity to meet other mums-to-be.

Now is the time to enrol at your local postnatal group or talk to your health visitor or practitioner about special events, meetings or exercise classes for new mums. From my own experience, once we had broken the ice over a few cups of tea, chatting, laughing and sharing the good and bad parts of motherhood with other women was a great delight and extremely reassuring. If you don't feel you are able to join a group, then talk to your health visitor and she will be able to help with any worries or perhaps put you in touch with a new mum nearby, who may be in a similar position.

### THE FOLLOWING TIPS SHOULD HELP

- don't be tempted to skip meals; they needn't be elaborate or grand. Try a baked potato topped with tuna or prawns, cottage cheese and lots of salad, or a grilled chop, with frozen vegetables and new potatoes, or pasta with pesto and steamed vegetables.
- accept offers of help and if none are forthcoming, don't be afraid to ask!
- try to take a nap when your baby sleeps, rather than race around catching up with chores. You and your baby are more important.
- if you find you and your baby are most fractious between 5 and 6 pm, then try to make a simple casserole and put it into the oven 2–3 hours earlier. That way you won't need to worry about cooking when you're feeling at your lowest ebb.
- share night feeds with your partner so that you can catch up on some sleep. If you are breastfeeding, express milk and put it in a bottle so that your partner can help with a feed.
- be kind to yourself – don't push too hard, you're not superwoman!
- babies vary in how often they want to feed. Bottle-fed babies tend to feed every 3–4 hours but may take a little time to settle into a routine.

# menu ideas

## DAY 1

**BREAKFAST**
Golden Granola with sliced banana and natural yogurt,
    page 60

**LUNCH**
Creamy Haddock & Spinach Chowder, page 76
Granary bread
Fruit

**SNACK**
Sticky Apricot Muesli Bar, page 141
Fruit tea

**SUPPER**
Sizzling Lamb Chops with Mixed Beans, page 102
Poached pears in cranberry juice and scoop of low-fat
    vanilla ice cream

## DAY 2

**BREAKFAST**
Poached Prunes, page 62
Toast

**LUNCH**
Dinner Jackets, page 75
Fruit yogurt

**SNACK**
Banana
Fruit tea

**SUPPER**
Easy Roast Chicken, page 111
Citrus Crush, page 133

## DAY 3

**BREAKFAST**
Fruit Smoothie, page 65, or a glass of orange juice
Boiled egg and soldiers

**LUNCH**
Jewel Box Salad with little gem lettuce and watercress,
    page 88
Fruit compôte with natural yogurt

**SNACK**
Pitta bread and hummus
Fruit tea

**SUPPER**
Kipper Kedgeree, page 94
Strawberry & Lime Brûlée, page 135

## FOOD FOR ALL THE FAMILY

**BREAKFAST**
Blueberry Pancakes, page 63

**LUNCH**
Cheat's Calzone with salad, page 72
Fruit yogurt

**SNACK**
Gingersnaps
Hot chocolate

**SUPPER**
Sausage Casserole, page 128
No-bake Lime & Blueberry Cheesecake, page 130

## NO TIME TO COOK DAY

**BREAKFAST**
Fruit salad
Granary toast
    or bowl of cereal and milk, plus dried fruit

**LUNCH**
Tuna Stackers, page 71
Fruit yogurt

**SNACK**
Currant bun
Hot chocolate

**SUPPER**
Mixed Bean & Chorizo Salad, page 84
Strawberry & Lime Brûlée, page 135

## MEAT-FREE DAY

**BREAKFAST**
Poached Prunes, page 62
Scrambled eggs on toast

**LUNCH**
Panzanella, page 86
Fruit

**SNACK**
Prune & Vanilla Muffin, page 138
Fruit tea

**SUPPER**
Mixed Mushroom Risotto, page 95
Baked peaches with fromage frais

## STORECUPBOARD STANDBY

**BREAKFAST**
Cereal with milk
Toast

**LUNCH**
Leek & Bacon Tortilla with salad, page 68
Fruit

**SNACK**
Spiced All-bran Bara Brith, page 140
Fruit tea

**SUPPER**
Moroccan Chickpea Stew, page 108
Plum Crumble, page 132

## FOOD FROM THE FREEZER

**BREAKFAST**
Mixed berries with Golden Granola, page 60
   or muesli and yogurt

**LUNCH**
Chunky Chilli Bean & Carrot Soup, page 81
Bread roll topped with grated cheese

**SNACK**
Prune & Vanilla Muffin, page 138

**SUPPER**
Creamy Fish Pie, page 119
Crumble topping sprinkled over gooseberries, rhubarb
   or apple, page 132

### FRIENDS FOR SUPPER
Quick Pesto, Pea & Broccoli Soup, page 79
Grilled Salmon with Celeriac Mash, page 92
No-bake Lime & Blueberry Cheesecake, page 130

# RECIPES

In this section you will find easy-to-prepare recipes for healthy breakfasts, quick snacks and tasty suppers. Some can be put together quickly after a day at work, others can be partly prepared and finished later – ideal for the later stages of pregnancy when you are feeling particularly tired. Recipes have nutritional and freezing tips and  suggestions on how to vary ingredients.

# breakfast boosters

Spoil yourself during pregnancy with these healthy breakfasts. There are quick and nutritious recipes for weekdays as well as suggestions for more leisurely weekend treats.

## GOLDEN GRANOLA

**This crunchy topping takes little time to prepare and makes a welcome change from plain muesli. It is delicious sprinkled over poached fruits, sliced bananas, strawberries or natural yogurt.**

2 tablespoons sunflower oil

2 tablespoons clear honey

2 tablespoons light muscovado sugar

25 g (1 oz) butter

4 tablespoons sesame seeds

4 tablespoons sunflower seeds

4 tablespoons flaked almonds

100 g (3½ oz) porridge oats

2 tablespoons wheatgerm (optional)

Serves 6

Put the oil, honey, sugar and butter into a frying pan and heat until the butter has melted and the sugar has dissolved. Stir in the seeds, almonds, oats and wheatgerm, if using. Mix well, then spread the oat mixture in a thin, even layer on a baking sheet.

Place the oat mixture in a preheated oven, 180°C (350°F), Gas Mark 4, for 8 minutes then stir well so that the paler mixture in the centre is moved to the outside edges of the baking sheet. Cook for a further 2–4 minutes until evenly browned, then leave to cool.

Break the oat mixture into pieces, place in an airtight jar or plastic container and seal tightly. The oat mixture can be stored in a cool cupboard for up to 2 weeks.

### BONUS POINTS
• The soluble fibre in oats is believed to help lower blood cholesterol levels.
• Wheatgerm is a healthy addition to this recipe as it is rich in B vitamins, iron, vitamin E and protein. Buy it plain or toasted from health food shops.

• If you have an ovenproof frying pan with a metal handle, there is no need to transfer the oat mixture to a baking sheet. Simply transfer the pan to the oven.
• Experiment by creating your own seed and nut mixture but keep the buttery base and the quantity of oats the same.

# POACHED PRUNES

**Prunes make an excellent start to the day. They're rich in vitamins, minerals and fibre, and help to relieve constipation, one of the not so nice side effects of pregnancy.**

2 rosehip tea bags
300 ml (½ pint) boiling water
200 g (7 oz) ready-to-eat dried, stoned
    prunes
1 tablespoon clear honey

**To serve:**
Greek yogurt
clear honey

Serves 2

---

• The prunes are delicious topped with a spoonful of Golden Granola (see page 60).
• The prunes can also be soaked in Earl Grey tea, but the caffeine in tea hinders the absorption of iron.

---

Put the tea bags into a bowl and pour the measured water over them. Leave the bags to infuse for 5 minutes, squeeze them out and discard, then add the prunes. Leave the prunes to soak for at least 30 minutes or overnight.

Stir the honey into the prunes and reheat, if liked, in a small saucepan or in a microwave for 2 minutes on full power.

Spoon the prunes into serving bowls and top with the yogurt and extra honey. Any remaining prunes can be stored in a plastic container for up to 3 days in the refrigerator.

## BONUS POINTS
• Dried prunes contain concentrated sugars, making them a good energy-boosting food. They also contain potassium, vitamin B6, iron and fibre as well as hydroxphenylisation derivatives. The latter stimulates the muscles of the large bowel, helping to relieve constipation.
• Many women go off tea and coffee when pregnant. Fruit teas make a great caffeine- and tannin-free alternative.

# BLUEBERRY PANCAKES

**These thick, American-style pancakes are a real treat topped with a dollop of thick Greek yogurt and a drizzle of maple syrup. To serve them as an indulgent dessert, add a scoop of real dairy vanilla ice cream instead of the yogurt.**

125 g (4 oz) self-raising flour
½ teaspoon baking powder
1 tablespoon icing sugar
1 medium egg
150 ml (¼ pint) semi-skimmed milk
125 g (4 oz) blueberries
1 tablespoon sunflower oil

**To serve:**
Greek yogurt
maple syrup

Serves 2

---

• For a storecupboard version of this dish, add some canned pitted red cherries or sultanas instead of the blueberries.

---

Put the flour, baking powder and sugar into a bowl. Add the egg and gradually whisk in the milk to make a smooth batter. Stir the blueberries into the batter.

Brush a little oil over the base of a large, heavy-based frying pan or griddle and heat. Place large spoonfuls of the batter, spaced well apart, in the pan or on the griddle and cook for 2 minutes or until bubbles begin to appear on the surface of the pancakes.

Loosen the pancakes with a palette knife, then turn them over and cook the other side until golden. Remove from the pan and keep hot in a clean tea towel. Continue making pancakes until all the batter is used up.

Pile the pancakes on to serving plates, top each one with a spoonful of Greek yogurt and drizzle with maple syrup.

## BONUS POINT
• Naturally sweet blueberries contain antibacterial compounds, which are particularly effective against some forms of E. coli, a major cause of gastrointestinal disorders, and can be a valuable aid against urinary infections, such as cystitis.

# FRUIT SMOOTHIE

**A great, refreshing pick-me-up, which is packed with vitamins and minerals to leave you feeling revitalized.**

1 papaya (paw paw), halved and
 deseeded
1 orange, peeled
1 banana, peeled
300 ml (½ pint) apple juice
ice, to serve (optional)

Serves 2

---

• A 400 g (13 oz) can of apricot
halves in natural juice can be used
instead of the papaya and apple
juice for a convenient
storecupboard pick-me-up.
• A little chopped fresh mint or a
squeeze of lime juice make a
refreshing addition.

---

Scoop out the papaya flesh with a spoon and put it into a food processor or blender. Holding the orange over the food processor, cut away the segments and add them with the juice from the membranes.

Thickly slice the banana and add to the papaya and orange with the apple juice. Blend together and pour into 2 glasses. Serve with ice, if liked.

## BONUS POINTS
• Papaya is a good source of vitamin C, and half a medium-sized fruit will provide an adult's daily requirement of the vitamin. It is also rich in beta carotene, the plant form of vitamin A.
• Papaya contains the enzyme papain, which aids digestion in the body.

# YOGURT & DATE SWIRL

**There's no need to keep these delicious yogurts just for breakfast, they make a great pud too.**

125 g (4 oz) stoned dates

2 dessert apples, quartered, cored and peeled

250 ml (8 fl oz) apple juice

300 g (10 oz) natural bio yogurt

Serves 4

---

• These yogurts can be stored in the refrigerator for up to 2 days.

• For a stripy effect, do not disturb the layers of date and yogurt.

• You could also make these yogurts with ready-to-eat dried apricots or prunes.

---

Roughly chop the dates and apples and put them into a saucepan with the apple juice. Bring to the boil, then cover and simmer for 10 minutes until soft. Leave to cool then spoon into a food processor or blender and blend until smooth.

Put alternate spoonfuls of date purée and yogurt into four glasses then swirl them together by running a small knife through the layers. Chill overnight or until ready to serve.

### BONUS POINTS
• Dried dates contain more potassium, niacin, copper, iron and magnesium than fresh ones.
• Don't be tempted to add sugar as dates are naturally sweet.

# THREE FRUIT SALAD

**Fresh, colourful and packed with vitamin C, this refreshing fruit salad is served in melon cups.**

1 small Charentais melon

1 pink or red grapefruit, peeled

2 kiwi fruits, peeled and halved
    lengthways

1 tablespoon chopped mint or a few
    tiny leaves

Serves 2

• The fruit can be prepared the night before and chilled in the refrigerator, but make sure to cover it tightly with clingfilm so that it doesn't dry out.

• Add orange segments or a few sliced strawberries instead of the kiwi fruit.

Cut a tiny slice off the top and bottom of the melon then cut it in half. Scoop out the seeds and then scoop the flesh on to a board. Stand the melon cups on two small plates, roughly chop the flesh, then put it into a bowl.

Holding the grapefruit over the bowl of melon, cut it into segments and squeeze the juice from the membrane. Thickly slice the kiwi fruits and add them to the bowl with the mint. Mix the fruit together then spoon it into the melon cups and chill until ready to serve.

## BONUS POINTS

• Just one medium orange or one kiwi fruit provides an adult's daily vitamin C requirement and is essential for the production of collagen, which helps keep the skin healthy and aids the body's fight against infection.

• Orange-fleshed melons are the most nutritious of all the melons, and contain beta carotenes, the plant form of vitamin A. These are antioxidants which may help to reduce cancer and heart disease. 100 g (3½ oz) of orange-fleshed melon provides half an adult's daily vitamin C allowance.

# snack lunches

**Eating small, regular meals can help to alleviate feelings of tiredness and nausea, so try not to skip lunch. If you're at home, settle in a comfy chair after lunch with a good book and rest for at least 30 minutes if you can.**

## LEEK & BACON TORTILLA

1 tablespoon olive oil

100 g (3 ½ oz) leeks, green part only, thinly sliced

3 rashers rindless streaky or back bacon, diced

125 g (4 oz) cooked potato, thinly sliced

4 eggs

1 tablespoon water

salt and pepper

Serves 2

---

- If you don't have any leftover cooked potato, thinly slice a small potato and cook it in a saucepan of boiling water for 3–5 minutes, until just tender, then continue with the recipe.
- For vegetarians, omit the bacon and add a few sliced mushrooms or frozen vegetables.
- For a picnic lunch, cut the tortilla into wedges and tuck it into pitta bread pockets with tomato chutney and salad.

**Although this tortilla serves two as a hot lunch, it is just as delicious eaten cold as a healthy snack to keep those mid-afternoon munchies at bay. Serve with a green salad – or bean and cucumber salad is particularly good for a change.**

Heat the oil in a medium frying pan with a metal handle. Add the leeks and bacon and fry for 5 minutes, until the leeks have softened and the bacon is golden. Add the potatoes and cook for 3 minutes, turning them gently, until golden.

Beat the eggs with the measured water and season with salt and pepper. Pour the mixture into the frying pan and cook until the underside is golden.

Place the tortilla under a preheated grill and cook until the top is golden and the eggs are well cooked all the way through. Cut into wedges and serve.

### BONUS POINT
- Eggs are a good source of protein, but have had a bad press for being one of the causes of salmonella poisoning. As long as pregnant women avoid raw eggs or dishes containing lightly cooked eggs, and use the eggs within the date stamp, they are perfectly safe.

# MUSHROOM BRUSCHETTA

**These tasty toasties are quick to put together, and if you have cooking facilities at work, they could be wrapped in foil and then finished under the grill when needed. Serve with a mixed leaf salad.**

1 ciabatta roll

2 teaspoons sun-dried tomato or black
    olive paste

1 tomato, chopped

4 small mushrooms, chopped

1 tablespoon olive oil

1 teaspoon pesto

2 tablespoons freshly grated Parmesan
    cheese

salt and pepper

basil leaves, to garnish (optional)

Serves 1

• Sliced French bread or a sliced
wholemeal or granary roll can be
used instead of ciabatta.

• To serve the bruschetta as
an informal starter with drinks,
increase the quantity of
ingredients as required.

Cut the ciabatta roll into 3–4 slices. Lightly toast the slices on both sides, then spread with the tomato paste.

Mix together the tomato, mushrooms, oil and pesto and season with salt and pepper. Spoon the mixture over the toast and sprinkle with the Parmesan. Place the bruschetta under a preheated hot grill and cook until piping hot. Garnish with the basil leaves, if using.

## BONUS POINT
• White bread is fortified with calcium, niacin, thiamin and iron and contains twice as much calcium as brown bread.

# TUNA STACKERS

**Liven up an everyday tuna sarnie with this triple-layered sandwich, packed with a crisp, crunchy salad and dressed in balsamic vinegar.**

100 g (3½ oz) can tuna in water, drained

2 teaspoons balsamic vinegar

3 slices granary bread

2 tablespoons low-fat cream cheese

¼ red pepper, deseeded and finely diced

2.5 cm (1 inch) piece of cucumber, finely diced

few watercress sprigs

salt and pepper

Serves 1

• Chopped celery or sweetcorn kernels can be used in place of the red pepper, while you could use rocket leaves or finely shredded lettuce instead of the watercress, if preferred.

• For a more unusual colour combination, use 2 slices of brown bread and 1 slice of white.

Mash the tuna with half the vinegar and season to taste with salt and pepper. Spread over 1 slice of bread, then top with a second slice.

Spread the second slice of bread with half the cream cheese and sprinkle with the red pepper, cucumber and the remaining vinegar. Add the watercress and season with salt and pepper. Spread the remaining cream cheese over the last slice of bread and place the cream cheese side down on top of the sandwich. Cut the sandwich into triangles and secure with cocktail sticks, if needed.

## BONUS POINTS

• Tuna makes a convenient, high-protein sandwich filling, and if you buy it canned in water, instead of oil, you will save 84 calories per 100 g (3½ oz) serving.

• Low-fat cream cheese makes a healthier alternative to butter, margarine or regular mayonnaise and contains calcium necessary for your baby's growing bones.

# CHEAT'S CALZONE

**Traditionally calzone is made with a soft pizza dough which is folded to encase the filling. Here, the base is made with a soft flour tortilla for a quick cheat. Serve the calzone with a salad.**

2 small soft flour tortillas

2 teaspoons sun-dried tomato paste

1 tomato, sliced

75 g (3 oz) mozzarella cheese, thinly
    sliced

few basil leaves, plus extra to garnish

4–6 young spinach leaves

1 tablespoon olive oil

salt and black pepper

Serves 1

---

• Try grated or sliced Cheddar cheese, chopped ham and mushrooms or your own favourite pizza topping combination.

• A little pesto can be used instead of the basil leaves and frozen spinach instead of fresh, but defrost it first and drain well.

• Individually wrap the remaining tortillas in the pack and freeze, then defrost at room temperature or in the microwave before use.

---

Rinse the tortillas with water to soften them, so they will fold and stick together, then place on a chopping board. Spread the tomato paste over half of each tortilla and arrange the tomato and mozzarella on top. Add the basil leaves and spinach and season with salt and pepper.

Fold each tortilla over the filling and press the edges together. (Don't worry if the edges do not stick in places.) Heat the oil in a frying pan, add the tortillas and fry for 1–2 minutes on each side, until golden. Transfer to a plate and serve.

## BONUS POINT

• If you find you go off milky drinks when pregnant, try to eat more cheese; 40 g (1½ oz) of hard cheese contains the same amount of calcium as 200 ml (7 fl oz) of milk which is vital for your baby's developing skeleton.

# BROAD BEAN & OLIVE TAPENADE

**Low in fat and a good source of fibre, this healthy spread is delicious served on lightly toasted ciabatta. It keeps well in the refrigerator and is just as tasty the day after making.**

½ small onion, finely chopped

1 garlic clove, chopped (optional)

1 teaspoon olive oil

200 g (7 oz) frozen broad beans

75 ml (3 fl oz) vegetable or chicken stock

2 tablespoons lemon juice

4 tablespoons chopped parsley

40 g (1½ oz) green or black pitted olives

salt and pepper

**To serve:**

toasted ciabatta bread

extra green or black olives

lemon wedges

Serves 2

• Frozen vegetables make a handy and nutritious addition to main courses and accompaniments. They are just as healthy as fresh, plus they do not need any preparation.
• If you're not an olive fan, then simply leave them out.
• Vary the herbs – try parsley mixed with mint, chives or rosemary.

Fry the onion and garlic, if using, in the oil for 5 minutes until softened. Add the beans and stock, simmer for 5 minutes and allow to cool.

Mash or process the beans in a food processor or blender with the lemon juice, parsley, olives, and salt and pepper, until they form a thick paste.

Serve warm or cold, spread on sliced and toasted ciabatta, garnished with olives and lemon wedges.

## BONUS POINTS

• Broad beans are high in soluble fibre which can help to reduce blood cholesterol levels.
• A 100 g (3½ oz) serving of tapenade supplies more than 25 per cent of an adult's daily requirement of phosphorus, necessary for healthy bones and teeth, and also provides protein, iron, B vitamins, and vitamins C and E.

# DINNER JACKETS

**Baked potatoes make a satisfying, low-fat lunch and require very little preparation.**

1 baking potato, about 250 g (8 oz)

100 g (3½ oz) cottage cheese

2 tablespoons frozen sweetcorn, defrosted

3 sun-dried tomatoes, diced

¼ green pepper, deseeded and diced

1 tablespoon chopped red onion

salt and pepper

Serves 1

Prick the potato and insert a skewer through the centre to speed up cooking. Place in a preheated oven, 200°C (400°F), Gas Mark 6, for 1¼ hours, until cooked through. Alternatively, prick the potato, place it on a sheet of kitchen paper and microwave on full power for 6 minutes until tender.

Meanwhile, mix the remaining ingredients. Cut the potato in half, pile the cottage cheese mixture on top and serve.

## BONUS POINT
• Contrary to their reputation, potatoes are not fattening; it's what you put on them that adds the calories and fat. This complex carbohydrate food provides plenty of energy, leaving you feeling full for long periods of time.

• Try topping a baked potato with a small, mashed avocado mixed with 2 tablespoons of fromage frais or cottage cheese and sprinkled with grilled crispy strips of streaky bacon.

• Mash a small 100 g (3½ oz) can of tuna or salmon with 3 tablespoons of cottage cheese or fromage frais, then stir in 1 chopped spring onion, ¼ diced red pepper and 2.5 cm (1 inch) piece of diced cucumber.

• Don't forget that old standby – canned baked beans and cheese. Serve with a glass of fresh orange juice to make a perfectly balanced meal.

# simply soups

Comforting and sustaining, soups can be made in advance and reheated when needed. They are a great pick-me-up when you are feeling tired or make a speedy, nutritious snack or lunch when a new baby is sleeping.

## CREAMY HADDOCK & SPINACH CHOWDER

25 g (1 oz) butter

1 tablespoon sunflower oil

1 onion, chopped

1 medium baking potato, diced

600 ml (1 pint) semi-skimmed milk

1 fish stock cube

2 bay leaves

freshly grated nutmeg

1 fillet of undyed smoked haddock, about 250 g (8 oz), cut in half

125 g (4 oz) young spinach leaves, stems removed and torn into pieces

salt and black pepper

4 grilled rindless streaky bacon rashers, to garnish (optional)

Serves 3

**American-style chowders are among the easiest soups to prepare, since the vegetables and fish are simply poached in milk and left chunky, resulting in a creamy, satisfying, calcium-packed soup. Serve with a chunk of crusty bread.**

Heat the butter and oil in a large, heavy-based saucepan, add the onion and fry gently for 5 minutes, until softened but not browned. Add the potato and fry for a further 5 minutes, stirring, until lightly browned.

Stir in the milk, stock cube, bay leaves, nutmeg and salt and pepper to taste. Add the haddock, then bring to the boil, cover and simmer for 10 minutes, until the haddock is cooked and flakes easily.

Lift the haddock out of the pan and place on a plate, peel off the skin and flake the flesh into pieces, carefully removing any bones, then set aside.

Add the spinach to the pan and cook for 2–3 minutes, until tender. Return the haddock to the pan and reheat.

Cut the grilled bacon into strips. Ladle the soup into bowls and garnish with the bacon, if using.

### BONUS POINT

• Spinach contains useful amounts of folic acid, vital in pre-conception care and during the first few months of pregnancy, since it has been known to prevent birth defects. Research suggests dark green, leafy vegetables and particularly spinach may help to prevent cancer. However, spinach is not as high in iron as was once believed.

---

• A fillet of salmon makes a good alternative to the smoked haddock, or try a mixture of green vegetables, perhaps broccoli, peas and strips of mangetout, in place of the spinach.

# GINGERED BUTTERNUT SQUASH & SWEET POTATO SOUP

2 tablespoons olive oil

1 large onion, finely chopped

1 butternut squash, about 875 g (1¾ lb), deseeded and cut into chunks

1 sweet potato, about 300 g (10 oz), cut into chunks

4 cm (1½ inch) piece of fresh root ginger, peeled and finely chopped

2 garlic cloves, chopped (optional)

900 ml (1½ pints) vegetable or chicken stock

450 ml (¾ pint) semi-skimmed milk

salt and pepper

**Croûtons:**

1 poppy seed bagel, cut into cubes

2 tablespoons olive oil

Serves 6

• The sweet potato helps to thicken the soup but you could use an ordinary potato, if preferred.
• This soup freezes well, which explains why the quantities given are greater than in other recipes. Freeze in individual portions in sealed and labelled plastic containers or bags.

**Velvety smooth, with a wonderful vibrant colour, this soup makes an ideal quick lunch and is smart enough to serve to friends, if dressed up with a swirl of cream.**

Heat the oil in a large, heavy-based saucepan, add the onion and fry for 5 minutes, until lightly browned. Add the squash, potato, ginger and garlic, if using, and fry for 3 minutes, stirring.

Pour in the stock, season with salt and pepper, and bring to the boil. Cover and simmer for 30 minutes, until reduced and thickened. Purée the soup in batches in a food processor or liquidizer until smooth. Return the soup to the pan, stir in the milk and set aside until ready to reheat.

Just before serving, put the cubed bagel into a plastic bag with the oil, toss together, and transfer to a baking sheet. Place in a preheated oven, 200°C (400°F), Gas Mark 6, for 10 minutes, until golden. Reheat the soup, ladle into bowls and serve sprinkled with the warm croûtons.

## BONUS POINTS

• Butternut squash and sweet potatoes are rich in beta carotene, the plant form of vitamin A, which is vital for normal cell division, growth and good eyesight, plus it is thought to help prevent some forms of cancer.
• Ginger has long been recognized as an aid to relieving the symptoms of morning sickness.
• Keep fat levels down by tossing the croûtons in oil in a plastic bag – this makes a little oil go much further.

# QUICK PESTO, PEA & BROCCOLI SOUP

2 tablespoons olive oil

1 onion, finely chopped

1 baking potato, about 275 g (9 oz), diced

1 garlic clove, chopped

200 g (7 oz) can tomatoes

900 ml (1½ pints) vegetable or chicken stock

175 g (6 oz) broccoli, cut into tiny florets and stalks sliced

125 g (4 oz) frozen peas

2 teaspoons pesto

salt and pepper

**To garnish:**

extra pesto

freshly grated Parmesan cheese

few basil leaves

Serves 4

• Four fresh, skinned and chopped tomatoes can be added to the soup instead of the canned variety, if preferred.

• To make the soup more substantial, add a small can of cannellini or white kidney beans or small soup pasta.

• Next time you roast a chicken, keep the carcass and use it to make a stock. Freeze the stock in handy portions for future use.

**Full of Italian flavour, this hearty vegetable soup is also a good source of vitamins and minerals, especially folate, vital for your growing baby. Serve with warm crusty bread.**

Heat the oil in a large, heavy-based saucepan, add the onion and fry for 5 minutes, until lightly browned. Add the potato and garlic and fry for 5 more minutes, stirring, until softened.

Add the tomatoes, stock and salt and pepper, then bring to the boil. Cover the pan and simmer for 10 minutes, until reduced and thickened. Add the broccoli, peas and pesto and simmer for a further 3–4 minutes, until the broccoli is just tender.

Ladle the soup into bowls, and garnish with a little extra pesto and sprinkle with the Parmesan and basil leaves.

## BONUS POINT

• 100 g (3½ oz) of cooked broccoli contains over half the recommended daily intake of vitamin C. The darker the floret the more vitamin C it contains.

# CHUNKY CHILLI BEAN & CARROT SOUP

**This warming soup has just a hint of chilli. It is made with ingredients that you will probably have to hand, so it makes a good standby for days when you feel too tired to shop.**

1 tablespoon olive oil

1 onion, chopped

2 carrots, diced

1 red pepper, cored, deseeded and diced

2 garlic cloves, chopped (optional)

1 small fresh or dried red chilli, deseeded and chopped

1 teaspoon cumin seeds

400 g (13 oz) can red kidney beans, drained and rinsed

500 g (1 lb) carton creamed tomatoes

600 ml (1 pint) vegetable or chicken stock

1 tablespoon brown sugar

salt and pepper

**To garnish:**

Greek yogurt

paprika

cumin seeds

Serves 4

---

• If you don't have a red pepper, you could add an extra carrot.

• Passata (sieved tomatoes) can be used instead of creamed tomatoes, if preferred.

---

Heat the oil in a large, heavy-based saucepan, add the onion and fry for 5 minutes, until lightly browned. Add the carrots, red pepper and garlic, if using, and fry for a further 3 minutes, until softened. Stir in the chilli and cumin and cook for 1 minute.

Add the kidney beans, creamed tomatoes, stock and sugar and season with salt and pepper. Bring to the boil, then cover and simmer for 30 minutes, until reduced and thickened.

Ladle the soup into bowls and top with a spoonful of yogurt and a sprinkling of paprika and cumin seeds.

## BONUS POINTS

• Carrots are unusual in that they are more nutritious cooked than raw. Cooking helps to break down the membranes, making it easier for the body to convert the beta carotene present in the carrots into vitamin A. If combined with fat in the same meal, then the body can absorb more than half of the beta carotene present, instead of just a quarter.

• Weight for weight, red peppers contain three times more vitamin C than oranges.

# VEGETABLE & LENTIL HOTCHPOTCH

1 onion

2 carrots, about 250 g (8 oz)

1 potato, about 250 g (8 oz)

1 parsnip, about 250 g (8 oz)

1 tablespoon sunflower oil

15 g (½ oz) butter

½ teaspoon turmeric

3 teaspoons mild curry paste

1.2 litres (2 pints) vegetable or
    chicken stock

75 g (3 oz) red lentils, rinsed

salt and pepper

a little chopped parsley, to garnish

Serves 4

**This budget-priced soup is a good way to use up the oddments from the vegetable rack and is tasty without being too spicy. A great healthy low-calorie lunch.**

Finely chop the onion and cut the carrots, potato and parsnip into fine dice. Heat the oil in a saucepan, add the onion and fry for 5 minutes, stirring until softened. Add the butter and the diced vegetables and fry for 5 minutes, stirring.

Stir in the turmeric and curry paste and cook for 1 minute then add the stock and lentils and season with salt and pepper. Bring to the boil, cover and simmer for 40 minutes until the lentils are soft. Ladle into bowls, sprinkle with a little parsley and serve with a sandwich.

## BONUS POINTS

• We should all try to include five portions of vegetables and fruit in our diet each day and making up batches of vegetable soup is a good way of doing this.
• Lentils are a good source of vegetable protein and soluble fibre, the type that can help to reduce blood cholesterol.

• Red, Puy and continental lentils do not need soaking before use, unlike dried pulses.
• If you don't have one of the vegetables listed above, substitute something that you do have, perhaps a little diced swede, some butternut squash, a courgette or some tomatoes.
• This soup will keep in the refrigerator for up to 3 days. Alternatively, allow it to cool and freeze in handy-sized individual portions.

# CREAMY BROCCOLI & ALMOND SOUP

15 g (½ oz) butter

1 tablespoon olive oil

1 onion, roughly chopped

150 g (5 oz) potato, peeled and finely diced

300 g (10 oz) broccoli

450 ml (¾ pint) vegetable or chicken stock

3 tablespoons flaked almonds

450 ml (¾ pint) semi-skimmed milk

100 g (3½ oz) low-fat cream cheese

salt and pepper

grated nutmeg, to taste

**To garnish:**

2 tablespoons flaked almonds, toasted

a little paprika

Serves 4

---

**Deceptively rich and creamy tasting, this speckled green soup is made with low-fat cream cheese and just a small knob of butter.**

Heat the butter and oil in a saucepan, add the onion and potato and fry for 5 minutes, stirring until softened but not browned. Cut the broccoli into florets and slice the stems, then add to the pan with the stock. Bring to the boil then reduce the heat, cover the pan and simmer for 8 minutes or until the vegetables are just tender.

Purée the soup in batches in a food processor or blender with the almonds, milk and cream cheese. Pour back into the pan, season with salt, pepper and nutmeg to taste. Reheat when needed and ladle the soup into bowls. To serve, garnish with toasted almonds and a little paprika.

**BONUS POINTS**

• One 100 g (3½ oz) portion of cooked broccoli provides just over half the recommended adult's daily intake of vitamin C. It is also a useful source of folate, vital if you are planning a pregnancy or are newly pregnant, and contains iron, potassium and beta carotene.

• Low-fat cream cheese and milk provide essential calcium for your baby's growing bones. Breast-feeding mums need to up their calcium intake from 700 mg to 1250 mg, or the equivalent of 1 litre (1¾ pints) of milk a day – so milky soups, drinks and sauces can be a useful addition to the menu.

---

• Keep a watchful eye on the clock while making this soup, as overcooking will result in a duller green soup.

• As toasting almonds is fiddly, cook more than you need and store the extra in an airtight container.

# main meal salads

A light, fresh-tasting and nutritious salad makes a perfect meal or snack during pregnancy, especially at the beginning when you may be feeling nauseous and tired, or towards the end when you need to eat little and often.

## MIXED BEAN & CHORIZO SALAD

75 g (3 oz) fresh or frozen green beans

200 g (7 oz) frozen baby broad beans

100 g (3½ oz) chorizo sausage, diced

½ small red onion, finely chopped

3 tablespoons chopped parsley

1 Little Gem lettuce, leaves separated (optional)

salt and pepper

**Dressing:**

2 tablespoons olive oil

juice of half lemon

1 garlic clove, crushed (optional)

Serves 2

• Diced ham or cooked gammon steak can be added to the salad instead of the chorizo.

• If following a meat-free diet, omit the chorizo and serve the salad as it is or with sliced hard-boiled eggs or freshly grated Parmesan, but do check that the cheese is suitable for vegetarians.

**Quick and easy to prepare, this salad makes a great supper dish and any leftovers can be stored in a small, insulated lunchbox and taken to work the next day. Serve with warm wholemeal bread.**

Plunge the green and broad beans into a saucepan of boiling water and cook for 3 minutes, until tender. Drain, rinse under cold running water, drain again, then cut the green beans into 3 pieces.

Place the chorizo in a grill pan and cook under a preheated hot grill for 6–8 minutes, turning occasionally, until browned and piping hot.

To make the dressing, mix together the oil, lemon juice and garlic, if using, in a salad bowl. Season to taste with salt and pepper and add the green and broad beans, the chorizo, onion and parsley, then toss together. Spoon the bean mixture into the lettuce leaves, if using.

### BONUS POINTS

• Broad beans are a useful addition to salads, since they are low in fat and high in soluble fibre, which may help to reduce blood cholesterol levels. They also contain useful protein.

• A dressing made with fresh lemon juice boosts its vitamin C content and reduces the amount of oil needed.

• Frozen vegetables contain the same amount of vitamins as fresh, and in the winter months may even provide greater amounts of certain nutrients.

• Pregnant women should not eat cured sausages, such as chorizo, unless they are cooked first. Make sure you buy them ready-wrapped and date stamped.

# PANZANELLA

**Based on the classic Italian salad, this peasant dish is a colourful combination of fresh tomatoes, black olives, hard-boiled eggs and golden croûtons, with a fresh basil and balsamic vinegar dressing.**

2 eggs

300 g (10 oz) tomatoes, cut into wedges

6 pitted black olives

2 sun-dried tomatoes in oil, drained
    and thinly sliced

salt and pepper

**Croûtons:**

1 small, crusty sesame roll, cut into
    cubes

2 tablespoons olive oil

**Dressing:**

1 tablespoon balsamic vinegar

a few torn basil leaves

Serves 2

Put the eggs into a small saucepan of water, bring to the boil and cook for 10 minutes, until hard boiled.

Meanwhile, put the cubes of bread into a plastic bag with the oil and toss together. Transfer the bread to a baking sheet and place in a preheated oven, 200°C (400°F), Gas Mark 6, for 8–10 minutes, until crisp and golden.

Drain the eggs and crack the shells. Fill the saucepan with cold water, put the eggs back in and leave them to cool.

Put the tomatoes, olives and sun-dried tomatoes into a salad bowl. Add the vinegar and basil and salt and pepper to taste, then toss together.

Cut the eggs into wedges and add to the salad with the warm croûtons, then spoon on to plates.

## BONUS POINTS
• Eggs are a valuable source of protein, but do make sure they are well cooked. Pregnant women should avoid raw or lightly cooked eggs.
• Tomatoes are rich in vitamin C as well as the carotenoid pigment lycopene, which gives them their red colour. Lycopene may help to protect against several types of cancer and heart disease as well as improve male fertility.

• The salad can be made in advance, but avoid adding the croûtons until the last minute or they will go soggy.
• If you dislike olives, then add a few blanched green beans, asparagus tips or even a small can of flaked tuna instead.

# ROASTED TOMATO & PEPPER SALAD

**Forget about limp lettuce leaves, this robust and hearty salad is filling and delicious. Serve it with warmed pitta bread.**

100 g (3½ oz) Puy lentils, rinsed
450 ml (¾ pint) vegetable stock
250 g (8 oz) cherry tomatoes on the vine
1 red pepper, quartered, cored and
    deseeded
1 tablespoon olive oil
1 orange, segmented
sea salt and pepper

**Dressing:**
1 tablespoon olive oil
1 tablespoon balsamic vinegar
1 teaspoon sun-dried tomato paste

Serves 2

---

• Sprinkle fresh herbs, such as chives, parsley or rosemary, over the salad, to add a new twist.
• This salad is ideal for those on a dairy-free vegetarian diet.

---

Put the lentils and stock into a saucepan. Bring to the boil, then simmer, uncovered, for 35 minutes or until the lentils are tender, topping up with more water if required.

Meanwhile, put the tomatoes on the vine in a small roasting tin with the pepper, skin-side uppermost. Drizzle over the oil and season with salt and pepper. Place in a preheated oven, 220°C (425°F), Gas Mark 7, for 10 minutes, until the skins have blistered.

To make the dressing, mix together the oil, vinegar, tomato paste and a little salt and pepper.

Drain the lentils, place in a salad bowl and combine with the dressing. Snip the roasted tomatoes off the vine and add to the salad with the pan juices and orange segments. Leave the pepper to cool, then peel off the skin and slice. Add to the salad, toss together and serve warm or chilled.

## BONUS POINTS
• Oranges and tomatoes contain essential folate, which is converted by the body into folic acid, vital if planning a pregnancy and in the early stages of pregnancy.
• Lentils are a good source of protein, but unlike animal proteins, they do not contain all eight essential amino acids. If you are a vegetarian, it is important to eat a wide range of vegetable proteins to get a good balance of the different amino acids.

# JEWEL BOX SALAD

**This colourful salad keeps well in the refrigerator, so can be made the night before and taken to work in an insulated container for a healthy lunch. It also makes a great picnic dish.**

75 g (3 oz) bulgar wheat, rinsed

3 tablespoons frozen peas

3 tablespoons frozen sweetcorn

200 ml (7 fl oz) hot vegetable or chicken stock

½ red pepper, cored, deseeded and diced

½ yellow pepper, cored, deseeded and diced

2 tomatoes, diced

125 g (4 oz) feta cheese, drained and cubed

2 tablespoons chopped mint

**Dressing:**

grated rind and juice of ½ lemon

1 tablespoon olive oil

salt and pepper

Serves 2

• Couscous could also be used as the base for this salad.

• Other cheeses, such as halloumi or mozzarella, can be used, or nuts or beans if you are looking for a non-animal source of protein.

Put the bulgar wheat and frozen vegetables into a large bowl, pour the hot stock over them and leave to soak for 10 minutes.

Meanwhile, make the dressing. Mix the lemon rind and juice, oil and salt and pepper in a salad bowl.

Add the peppers, tomatoes and feta to the dressing with the mint. Drain the bulgar wheat and vegetables, if necessary, and add to the pepper mixture. Toss together and chill until ready to serve.

## BONUS POINTS

• Bulgar wheat is a low-fat, complex carbohydrate, which takes a long time to digest, keeping energy levels up and leaving you feeling full for longer. It also contains some of the B vitamins, plus copper and iron.

• Although feta cheese is quite salty, a little goes a long way. Mums-to-be should make sure it is made with pasteurized milk and, if vegetarian, made with a non-rennet starter.

# ORIENTAL CHICKEN SALAD

2 boneless, skinless chicken breasts, about 150 g (5 oz) each

2 tablespoons soy sauce

2 teaspoons sunflower oil

1 small fennel bulb, quartered, cored and separated into leaves

2 carrots, about 200 g (7 oz), cut into thin sticks

75 g (3 oz) mangetout, halved

1 tablespoon sesame seeds (optional)

**Dressing:**

4 teaspoons sunflower oil

2 teaspoons rice vinegar or white wine vinegar

2.5 cm (1 inch) piece of fresh root ginger, peeled and finely chopped

Serves 2

---

• The chicken breasts can be left whole, marinated and then grilled, if preferred. Do make sure you increase the cooking times and check the chicken is thoroughly cooked before serving.

• Beansprouts or shredded Chinese leaves could also be added to this salad, if liked.

• For an attractive garnish, cut 2 spring onions into 3 pieces, then into fine strips. Soak the strips of onion in cold water, so that they curl, and sprinkle them over the salad just before serving.

**This Chinese-inspired salad makes a refreshing change to the regular leafy variety. The marinated chicken complements the delicate aniseed flavour of the fennel and light ginger dressing.**

Cut the chicken breasts lengthways into 4 thin slices, then halve each of these. Put the chicken slices into a shallow bowl with the soy sauce and the oil. Cover with a plate or clingfilm and leave to marinate in the refrigerator for 30 minutes.

Meanwhile, bring a pan of water to the boil, add the fennel and carrots and cook for 1 minute. Add the mangetout and cook for 30 seconds more. Drain, rinse with cold water and drain again.

To make the dressing, mix the oil, vinegar and ginger in a salad bowl. Add the vegetables and toss together.

Lift the chicken out of the marinade and place in a grill pan. Sprinkle with the sesame seeds, if using, and cook under a preheated grill, placed 5 cm (2 inches) away from the heat, for 4 minutes. Turn the chicken and spoon over the remaining marinade. Grill for a further 4 minutes, until cooked through, then cut into small pieces and add to the salad. Serve warm or cold.

## BONUS POINT

• Chicken is a good source of protein, which is essential for both you and your developing baby. Protein helps in the growth and repair of muscles, bones, hair and fingernails.

# HALLOUMI & RADICCHIO SALAD

**This attractive, eye-catching, red leaf salad is peppered with strips of radish, capers and fresh herbs, then topped with golden slices of halloumi cheese.**

½ small radicchio, torn into small pieces

½ red leaf lettuce, torn into small pieces

50 g (2 oz) radishes, cut into strips

2 tomatoes, chopped

2 tablespoons olive oil

175 g (6 oz) halloumi cheese, drained and sliced

**Dressing:**

2 teaspoons capers, drained (optional)

4 tablespoons lemon juice

3 tablespoons chopped oregano

salt and pepper

Serves 2

Wash the salad leaves well then mix with the radishes and tomatoes, and divide between 2 serving plates.

Heat the oil in a frying pan and fry the halloumi for 1–2 minutes on each side, until golden. Place the halloumi on top of the leaves.

Mix together the capers, lemon juice, oregano and salt and pepper, then spoon over the salad just before serving.

## BONUS POINTS

• Salad leaves are a useful source of folate, which is converted by the body into folic acid, and are important for those women planning a baby or who are in the early stages of pregnancy, as they help to prevent birth defects.

• Deeply pigmented leaves contain beta carotene, a useful antioxidant. The dark outer lettuce leaves may contain up to 50 times more beta carotene than the paler ones found in the centre.

• Herbalists believe that lettuce leaves have a calming effect and can aid sleep.

• Like feta, halloumi is quite salty so be careful when seasoning the salad.

• Other fresh herbs, such as parsley, chives, basil or marjoram, also work well in this salad.

• If you can't find radicchio, then use a mixed bag of salad leaves instead.

# dinner at the double

Sharing a meal with your partner is a great time to catch up on news, even if you both get home late after work. If you share the preparation and cooking, a meal can be ready in just a matter of minutes, or simply halve the recipes if you are cooking for one.

## GRILLED SALMON WITH CELERIAC MASH

250 g (8 oz) celeriac, diced

300 g (10 oz) canned cannellini beans, drained and rinsed

juice of 1 lemon

2 tablespoons chopped chives

pinch of grated nutmeg

2 salmon steaks, about 150 g (5 oz) each

2 teaspoons olive oil

125 g (4 oz) young spinach leaves, stems removed

2 teaspoons balsamic vinegar

salt and pepper

chives, to garnish (optional)

Serves 2

---

• Potatoes or butternut squash, or even carrots, could be used instead of celeriac, if preferred.

---

**This upmarket fish supper is quick and easy to put together, and the beneficial fish oils in the salmon are good for your – and your baby's – brain.**

Cook the celeriac in a saucepan of boiling water for 15 minutes, until just tender. Drain the beans and mash with the lemon juice, chopped chives, nutmeg and salt and pepper.

Meanwhile, place the salmon steaks on a grill rack, drizzle with the oil and season to taste with salt and pepper. Cook the salmon under a preheated grill, placing the rack 5 cm (2 inches) away from the heat, for 5 minutes. Turn the salmon over and cook the other side for a further 2 minutes, or until the fish flakes when pressed with a knife.

Meanwhile, steam the spinach for 2 minutes, until just wilted. Reheat the mash, if necessary, spoon on to plates and top with the spinach. Remove the skin from the salmon and place it skinned-side down on the spinach. Drizzle with balsamic vinegar and garnish with extra chives, if using.

### BONUS POINTS

• Salmon contains twice as many calories as white fish, so grill or steam whenever possible. However, as with other oily fish, it contains valuable omega-3 fatty acids, which are essential for brain formation, healthy development of the eyes and ensuring that pregnancies go to full term.

• Spinach contains useful amounts of folate (folic acid), vital for women hoping to become pregnant, as well as those in the early stages of pregnancy.

# KIPPER KEDGEREE

**Health practitioners and nutritionists regularly encourage us to eat more oily fish, but it is especially important during pregnancy as it can aid the development of your baby's brain.**

750 ml (1¼ pints) water

150 g (5 oz) easy-cook brown rice

2 bay leaves

½ teaspoon turmeric

5 cardamom pods, crushed

2 eggs

2 kipper fillets, about 250 g (8 oz) in total

75 g (3 oz) frozen peas

15 g (½ oz) butter

½ bunch of spring onions, sliced

½ teaspoon cumin seeds, roughly crushed

3 tablespoons single cream

pepper

Serves 2

• Many people dislike kippers because of the bones, but by flaking the fish and removing the bones before serving, there's no excuse!

• Kippers can be quite salty, so there is no need to add additional salt until you have tasted the finished dish.

Pour the measured water into a large saucepan, bring to the boil and add the rice, bay leaves, turmeric, cardamom pods and pepper to taste. Return to the boil, then reduce the heat and simmer, covered, for 20 minutes, until the rice is tender and most of the water has been absorbed.

Meanwhile, put the eggs into a small saucepan and cover with cold water; bring to the boil and cook for 10 minutes. Drain, crack the shells and cover with cold water. Remove the shells when the eggs are cool enough to handle.

Add the kippers and peas to the rice, top up with a little extra water if needed, cover, and cook for a further 5 minutes, until the fish flakes easily. Carefully lift out the kippers, remove the skin and flake the flesh into pieces, removing any bones.

Heat the butter in a saucepan and fry the spring onions and cumin for 2 minutes, until softened. Stir the onions into the rice with the flaked fish and cream. Spoon on to plates and top with the eggs, cut into wedges.

## BONUS POINTS
• People who eat oily fish, such as kippers, herrings, mackerel and salmon, once a week are less likely to suffer from heart disease or strokes, and this also includes your unborn baby.
• The starch in brown rice is digested more slowly, leaving you feeling full for longer.
• Frozen peas are just as nutritious as fresh, and provide useful amounts of folate (folic acid) and fibre.

# MIXED MUSHROOM RISOTTO

**This creamy vegetarian risotto is tasty and substantial enough to appeal to even the most committed meat-eater.**

6 dried shiitake mushrooms

200 ml (7 fl oz) boiling water

2 tablespoons olive oil

1 onion, chopped

2–3 garlic cloves, chopped

150 g (5 oz) risotto rice, rinsed
and drained

600 ml (1 pint) hot vegetable or
chicken stock

a few stalks of fresh thyme or a pinch of
dried thyme

2 tablespoons dry or sweet sherry

2 large, flat mushrooms

25 g (1 oz) butter

2 tablespoons chopped parsley or
parsley and chives

salt and pepper

Parmesan cheese shavings, to garnish
(optional)

Serves 2

---

• Serve thin slices of grilled
garlicky chicken or grilled lamb
chops or strips of crispy bacon in
place of the large mushrooms.
• Risotto is also delicious flavoured
with rosemary or sage instead of
thyme, or use white wine or cider
in place of the sherry.

---

Put the dried mushrooms into a bowl, cover with the measured water and leave to soak for 15 minutes, until softened.

Meanwhile, heat all but 2 teaspoons of the oil in a frying pan, add the onion and half of the garlic and fry for 5 minutes, until softened.

Stir in the rice and cook for 1 minute, then add 2 ladlefuls of the stock and the thyme and season with salt and pepper. Bring to the boil, then reduce the heat and simmer until the stock is absorbed, then add another ladleful of stock. Continue adding stock and simmering until 450 ml (¾ pint) stock has been absorbed. This should take about for 10 minutes.

Drain the shiitake mushrooms, reserving the soaking water, and slice them. Add the mushrooms to the risotto with the soaking water and sherry. Simmer for a further 10–15 minutes, stirring occasionally, until the rice is creamy and tender. Top up with the remaining stock as needed.

Meanwhile, 5 minutes before the rice is ready, place the large mushrooms on a piece of foil and fold up the edges. Dot the mushrooms with butter and spoon the rest of the garlic and oil over the top. Season and cook under a preheated grill, placed 5 cm (2 inches) away from the heat, for 4–5 minutes, until tender.

Spoon the rice on to plates, top with the mushrooms and buttery juices. Sprinkle with the parsley and Parmesan, if using.

## BONUS POINT

• While it is important to watch the amount of alcohol you consume while pregnant, alcohol evaporates when it is heated but imparts a mellow and concentrated flavour, giving a simple supper a lift.

# STICKY GLAZED GAMMON WITH MANGO SALSA

**The fresh and fruity salsa lends a new twist to the classic pub favourite, grilled gammon with pineapple. Serve with oven-baked jacket chips or garlic bread.**

2 smoked gammon steaks, about
    200 g (7 oz) each
1 tablespoon marmalade
1 teaspoon Dijon mustard
2 teaspoons sunflower oil
salt and pepper
Cos lettuce leaves, to garnish (optional)

**Salsa:**
1 small mango
½ small red onion, finely chopped
5 cm (2 inch) piece of cucumber, finely
    chopped
2 tomatoes, finely chopped
small bunch of coriander, finely
    chopped
75 g (3 oz) sweetcorn, defrosted if
    frozen
rind and juice of 1 lime

Serves 2

- Add a little chopped fresh red chilli to the salsa, if liked.
- This salsa also tastes good with grilled pork chops or griddled chicken breasts.

To make the salsa, place the mango on a chopping board and cut away the 2 sides, leaving the oval stone in the centre. Make criss-cross cuts in the flesh of the large slices, then turn them inside out and cut away the diced mango. Cut away any remaining mango flesh from around the stone, peel and dice.

In a bowl, mix together the onion, cucumber, tomatoes and coriander, then add the mango, sweetcorn, lime rind and juice and a little salt and pepper. Set aside.

Snip the rind on the gammon steaks to prevent them curling, then put the steaks into a grill pan. Mix the marmalade, mustard, oil and salt and pepper and spread this marinade over the steaks.

Cook the steaks under a preheated grill for 10 minutes, turning once, until the fat is golden.

Place the steaks on serving plates, garnish with lettuce leaves, if using, and add a spoonful of the salsa.

### BONUS POINTS
- Fruit is higher in vitamin C when uncooked.
- Iron deficiency can leave you feeling tired and lead to anaemia. Red meat is a good source of iron, but avoid liver, since its vitamin A content is too high for pregnant women.

# GRILLED MACKEREL WITH HOT RED CABBAGE SALAD

**Complement the robust flavour of grilled mackerel with this crunchy red cabbage stir-fry with apple and caraway seeds.**

2 fresh headless mackerel, about 250 g (8 oz) each, gutted

1 teaspoon sunflower oil

½ red onion, thinly sliced

175 g (6 oz) red cabbage, finely shredded

1 red dessert apple, cored, peeled and diced

½ teaspoon caraway seeds

2 teaspoons balsamic vinegar

1 teaspoon light muscovado sugar

salt and pepper

chopped parsley, to garnish (optional)

Serves 2

Make 3 cuts across each side of the mackerel and place in a foil-lined grill pan. Fold up the edges of the foil to catch the juices, and shield the tails with extra foil. Cook under a preheated grill, placed 5 cm (2 inches) away from the heat, for 8–10 minutes, turning once, until the fish flakes when pressed with a knife.

Meanwhile, heat the oil in a frying pan or wok, add the onion and cabbage and stir-fry over a high heat for 5 minutes. Add the apple, caraway seeds, vinegar, sugar and salt and pepper and stir-fry for a further 3 minutes.

Spoon the cabbage mixture on to plates, top with the mackerel and sprinkle with parsley, if using.

## BONUS POINT
• Mackerel is rich in omega-3 fatty acids and vitamin D, as well as selenium, which is vital when planning to conceive and for the sexual development of your unborn child.

• Choose fish with glossy looking scales and skin and well-rounded, bright eyes. Use on the day of purchase and always rinse well with plenty of cold water before cooking.

• As mackerel contains more natural fish oils than white fish, there is no need to add any extra oil when grilling or barbecuing.

# PANCETTA-WRAPPED ROAST PORK

2 x 7.5 cm (3 inch) pieces of pork tenderloin, about 325 g (11 oz) in total, fat trimmed

6 slices of pancetta, about 50 g (2 oz)

2 teaspoons sun-dried tomato paste

6–8 sage leaves, plus extra to garnish (optional)

oil, to grease

**Polenta:**

450 ml (¾ pint) water

75 g (3 oz) quick-cook, instant polenta

25 g (1 oz) butter

50 g (2 oz) rocket and watercress salad

1 tablespoon chopped sage

salt and pepper

Serves 2

• Look for sliced pre-packed pancetta, or use 2 slices of smoked, streaky bacon instead, and stretch with the back of a knife.

• If you haven't used polenta before, look for "quick-cook" or "instant" dried polenta in boxes. In this recipe, the plastic-wrapped sausage of ready-cooked polenta is unsuitable.

• If you have a fan-assisted oven, reduce the oven temperature to 200°C (400°F), Gas Mark 6, and check the pork after 15 minutes.

**Italian-inspired roast pork, which takes only 20 minutes to roast, served on a bed of buttery polenta ... sounds too good to be true!**

Put 3 slices of pancetta, slightly overlapping, on a board and place a piece of pork in the centre. Spread the pork with the tomato paste, turning it to coat all sides. Tuck 3–4 sage leaves, if using, around the pork, then wrap it in the pancetta and secure with a cocktail stick. Repeat with the second piece of pork.

Transfer the pork to a small oiled roasting tin. Roast in a preheated oven, 220°C (425°F), Gas Mark 7, for 20 minutes, spooning the juices over the meat after 10 minutes.

Just before serving, pour the measured water into a saucepan, bring to the boil and stir in the polenta. Cook, stirring, for 2–3 minutes, until thick. Stir in the butter, the rocket and watercress salad, sage, salt and pepper and the juices from the roasting tin. Cook for 1 minute, then spoon on to plates and top with the pork. Remove the cocktail sticks and garnish with sage leaves, if using.

### BONUS POINT

• A high-protein food, pork is a good source of B vitamins, iron and zinc, which is needed by the body for the make-up of DNA and RNA, growth and the development of the reproductive organs in your unborn child. As with chicken, make sure pork is thoroughly cooked before serving.

# LINGUINE WITH PEAS & PANCETTA

**This super speedy supper can be on the table in the same time that it takes to reheat a ready-prepared meal!**

150 g (5 oz) dried linguine

1 tablespoon olive oil

75 g (3 oz) pancetta, diced

100 g (3½ oz) frozen petit pois

4 tablespoons single cream

3 teaspoons pesto

shavings Parmesan cheese

salt and pepper

basil leaves, to garnish (optional)

Serves 2

Bring a large saucepan of salted water to the boil, add the pasta, return to the boil and cook for 6–7 minutes, until just tender.

Meanwhile, heat the oil in a frying pan, add the pancetta and fry for 4–5 minutes, stirring, until browned. Add the peas and cook for 2 minutes, then stir in the cream, pesto and salt and pepper and cook for 1 minute.

Drain the pasta, add to the frying pan and toss with the sauce. Spoon into shallow bowls and sprinkle with Parmesan and basil leaves, if using.

## BONUS POINT
• The humble frozen pea contains a surprising number of nutrients, including vitamin C, folate, thiamin, phosphorus, protein and fibre, and often at higher levels than its fresh counterpart.

• Pancetta is an Italian cured bacon and is now readily available, diced, in supermarkets alongside the pre-packed ham and salami. If you can't find it, then use diced streaky or back bacon instead.

• If using fresh pasta, don't forget to reduce the cooking time to just 1–2 minutes.

# SIZZLING LAMB CHOPS WITH MIXED BEANS

4 lamb cutlets, about 425 g (14 oz)

4 teaspoons clear honey

150 g (5 oz) frozen broad beans

75 g (3 oz) frozen green beans

50 g (2 oz) frozen peas

2 tablespoons chopped mint

2 teaspoons balsamic vinegar

salt and pepper

tiny mint leaves, to garnish (optional)

Serves 2

• Vary the herbs depending on what is available either in the garden or in the shops – sage, rosemary, chives, tarragon or a mixture of herbs are delicious tossed with the cooked beans.

• Garlic fans may like to sprinkle a chopped garlic clove over the cutlets before grilling.

• The bean mixture is delicious served with roast lamb and parsnips, or grilled gammon steaks, and even salmon or cod steaks.

• Canned flageolet or cannellini beans can be used instead of frozen broad beans, if preferred.

• Apricot jam, marmalade or redcurrant jelly can be used in place of the honey.

**This quick and healthy supper is a good source of protein and fibre, and is cooked without any additional fat. Why not barbecue the chops and enjoy a summer supper in the garden with a glass of chilled mineral water and some ciabatta bread.**

Arrange the cutlets in a foil-lined grill pan. Season with salt and pepper, drizzle with honey and cook under a preheated hot grill, 5 cm (2 inches) away from the heat, for 4 minutes on each side or until the cutlets have browned and are cooked through.

Meanwhile, cook the frozen vegetables in a saucepan of boiling water for 4 minutes. Drain and return to the pan. Stir in the mint, vinegar and meat juices. Spoon on to plates, top with the cutlets and garnish with the mint leaves, if using.

## BONUS POINTS

• Red meat is a rich source of "haem" iron, which is more readily absorbed by the body than the type of iron found in vegetables and cereals.

• It is important to increase the amount of folic acid in the diet when hoping to conceive and particularly during the early stages of pregnancy. Green vegetables are a good source and frozen ones make a great fuss-free and healthy alternative to fresh ones.

• Pregnancy can play havoc with the bowels, so it is important to eat enough fibre. Frozen broad beans are ideal as there's no preparation and their soluble fibre content may help to reduce blood cholesterol levels. They are also a good source of beta carotene, which the body converts to vitamin A.

# GRILLED SARDINES WITH CORIANDER & LIME SAUCE

**Sardines are surprisingly cheap to buy and make a nutritious summer supper. They can be barbecued or grilled, as preferred. Serve with a green salad and new potatoes.**

6 fresh sardines, about 500 g (1 lb), gutted and descaled

2 limes

4 teaspoons olive oil, plus extra to grease

15 g (½ oz) coriander leaves, chopped

salt and pepper

Serves 2

• Use fish on the day of purchase, and buy only from a reputable fish shop or supermarket. You could also ask the fishmonger to prepare it for you.
• As sardines contain a fair amount of oil, leave the salad and potatoes plain.

Rinse the fish under cold running water; rub away any remaining scales with your fingertips and check that the insides are clean. Line a grill rack with foil. Oil the foil, then drain the fish, dry with kitchen paper and place on the foil. Fold the edges of the foil to catch any juices and shield the tails with an extra strip of foil.

Put the sardines under a preheated grill, 5 cm (2 inches) away from the heat, and cook for 3 minutes on each side, until golden and the fish flake easily when pressed with a knife. Transfer to serving plates. Cut one of the limes into wedges and squeeze the juice from the second. Mix the juice, oil, coriander and salt and pepper and spoon over the sardines.

## BONUS POINTS
• Fresh sardines are an excellent source of the antioxidant selenium, which aids fertility and growth as well as zinc, which is important in the development of the ovaries and testes.
• The natural oils in sardines contain omega-3 fatty acids, which aid brain development in your unborn child, while olive oil is rich in omega-6 fatty acids and monounsaturated fatty acids, thought to reduce blood cholesterol.

# HOISIN GLAZED BEEF WITH STIR-FRIED VEGETABLES

**Packed with vitamins and minerals, this colourful stir-fry is a good way to get a small amount of meat to go a long way.**

1 sheet egg noodles, about 90 g (3¼ oz)

1 tablespoon sunflower oil

1 carrot, cut into sticks

½ red pepper, cored, deseeded and cut into sticks

75 g (3 oz) button mushrooms, sliced

300 g (10 oz) rump steak, fat trimmed and thinly sliced

2 spring onions, trimmed and thickly sliced

2 tablespoons hoisin sauce

3 tablespoons water

100 g (3½ oz) pak choi, or 2 heads, thickly sliced

Serves 2

Soak the noodles in boiling water or cook in a saucepan of boiling water as directed on the pack. Drain and keep warm.

Meanwhile, heat the oil in a wok or heavy-based frying pan, add the carrot, red pepper and mushrooms and stir-fry for 2 minutes. Add the steak and spring onions and stir-fry for 2–3 minutes, until the steak has browned.

Add the hoisin sauce and the measured water, then add the pak choi and cook for 1 minute, until the green leaves have just wilted.

Spoon the drained noodles into bowls, top with the stir-fry and serve.

**BONUS POINT**

• Stir-frying helps to preserve the nutritional content of foods, since cooking times are kept to a minimum.

---

• Serve the beef with rice, if preferred.

• Garnish with thin strips of spring onion, that have been chilled in cold water until they curl.

• Chinese leaves or spinach could be used instead of the pak choi.

# make now, eat later

If you've recently given birth or are in the final stages of pregnancy, it may be more convenient to prepare supper earlier in the day, when you feel less tired, and finish it just before eating.

## LAMB & RED BEAN KOFTAS

### Koftas:

1 small onion

1 garlic clove, chopped

250 g (8 oz) lean minced lamb

200 g (7 oz) can red kidney beans, drained and rinsed

¼ teaspoon ground allspice

3 tablespoons fresh breadcrumbs

1 egg yolk

12–16 bay leaves, depending on size

olive oil

salt and pepper

### Cucumber relish:

5 cm (2 inch) piece of cucumber, diced

1 kiwi fruit, diced

1 tablespoon chopped mint

few flakes of dried chilli (optional)

### To serve:

4 pitta breads

shredded lettuce

150 g (5 oz) natural yogurt

Serves 2

**These couldn't be easier to make; the ingredients for these mini meatballs are simply whizzed together in a food processor, then they are threaded on to skewers and left in the refrigerator until ready to cook.**

Put all the ingredients for the koftas, except the bay leaves and oil, into a food processor. Season with salt and pepper and blend together. With damp hands, shape into 20 small balls and thread on to 4 metal or wooden skewers. Place on a baking sheet, tuck the bay leaves underneath and between the meatballs and loosely cover with clingfilm, then refrigerate.

Mix together the relish ingredients in a small bowl, cover with clingfilm, and refrigerate until required.

Brush the koftas with oil and cook under a preheated grill or on a barbecue for 12–15 minutes, turning occasionally, until they are browned and cooked through.

To serve, sprinkle the pitta breads with water and grill or barbecue until puffy. Make a cut lengthways in the pittas and, discarding the bay leaves, fill with the koftas, lettuce, relish and yogurt.

### BONUS POINTS
• Just 1 kiwi fruit supplies an adult's daily requirement of vitamin C.
• Lamb is rich in protein, B vitamins, plus the essential minerals zinc and iron, which are vital in pregnancy.

---

• If you don't have a food processor, then mince the ingredients for the koftas or make them in batches in a blender, adding an egg yolk at the end.

• The koftas can be wrapped in large, flat Middle Eastern bread or soft tortillas, if preferred.

• Keep a handy supply of fresh breadcrumbs in the freezer and use straight from the freezer.

• Raw koftas may be frozen on wooden skewers.

# MOROCCAN CHICKPEA STEW

**This recipe makes use of storecupboard ingredients, so if you don't feel up to shopping then this supper dish is ideal. Any leftovers can be served with bread the following day.**

1 tablespoon olive oil

1 onion, finely chopped

1 garlic clove, chopped

2.5 cm (1 inch) piece of fresh root
    ginger, peeled and grated

½ teaspoon turmeric

½ teaspoon paprika

1 teaspoon coriander seeds

1 teaspoon cumin seeds

400 g (13 oz) can chickpeas, drained

400 g (13 oz) can chopped tomatoes

150 ml (¼ pint) vegetable stock

2 carrots, diced

3 tablespoons sultanas

salt and pepper

natural yogurt, to serve

paprika, to garnish (optional)

**Couscous:**

100 g (3½ oz) couscous

1 tablespoon olive oil

250 ml (8 fl oz) boiling water

2 tablespoons lemon juice

3 tablespoons chopped mint or parsley

Serves 2–3

Heat the oil in a heavy-based saucepan, add the onion and fry for 5 minutes, stirring occasionally, until just browned. Stir in the garlic, ginger, turmeric and paprika.

Crush the coriander and cumin seeds using a pestle and mortar, add to the pan and cook for 1 minute.

Add the chickpeas, tomatoes, stock, carrots and sultanas and season with salt and pepper. Bring to the boil, stirring, then cover and simmer gently for 30 minutes, until reduced and slightly thickened. Set aside until ready to reheat.

To finish, put the couscous in a bowl, add the oil and pour over the measured water. Cover and leave to stand for 5 minutes. Meanwhile, reheat the chickpea stew.

Add the lemon juice, herbs and salt and pepper to the couscous and fluff up with a fork. Spoon on to plates with the chickpea stew. Top each serving with a spoonful of yogurt and a sprinkling of paprika, if using.

## BONUS POINT
• Chickpeas are high in fibre, so can help to relieve the symptoms of constipation during pregnancy.

---

• Frozen herbs make a convenient alternative to fresh, especially during the winter months. Buy ready-frozen herbs or freeze your own. Alternatively, try growing pots of fresh herbs by the back door or in window boxes.

• The chickpea stew freezes well; pack in individual portions in plastic containers.

---

# SAFFRON STEW

**Saffron is expensive, but a little goes a long way and transforms these simple Mediterranean vegetables into a bistro-style supper when served with slices of warm garlic bread.**

1 tablespoon olive oil

1 onion, chopped

½ red pepper, deseeded and roughly chopped

½ yellow pepper, deseeded and roughly chopped

2 small courgettes, about 175 g (6 oz), thickly sliced

1 garlic clove, chopped

400 g (13 oz) can cannellini beans, drained and rinsed

4 tomatoes, skinned and roughly chopped

1 tablespoon tomato purée

250 ml (8 fl oz) vegetable stock

large pinch saffron threads

salt and pepper

few black olives, to garnish (optional)

Serves 2

• Use a 200 g (7 oz) can of tomatoes, if preferred.
• This stew works well with other types of vegetables. Try sliced fennel, celery or mushrooms.
• To freeze, allow to cool after paragraph 2, then pack into a plastic container or individual plastic bags.

Heat the oil in a heavy-based saucepan, add the onion and fry for 5 minutes, until softened and lightly browned. Add the peppers, courgettes and garlic and cook for 2 minutes.

Add the beans, tomatoes, tomato purée, stock and saffron and season with salt and pepper. Bring to the boil, cover, and simmer for 10 minutes, then set aside until ready to reheat.

To finish, reheat the stew for 5 minutes, ladle into bowls and top with the black olives, if using.

### BONUS POINT
• The phytochemical lycopene, responsible for the red colouring in tomatoes, is thought to improve the quality of sperm, so get your man to eat plenty of tomatoes if planning a baby!

# EASY ROAST CHICKEN

2 chicken breasts, on the bone, about
    300 g (10 oz) each

4 bay leaves

1 orange

200 g (7 oz) shallots

200 g (7 oz) parsnips, cut into chunky
    pieces

200 g (7 oz) carrots, cut into chunky
    pieces

400 g (13 oz) new potatoes, halved,
    if large

6 garlic cloves, unpeeled

3 tablespoons olive oil

3 teaspoons clear honey

salt flakes and pepper

orange wedges, to serve

bay leaves, to garnish

**Gravy:**

2 teaspoons cornflour

1 teaspoon Dijon mustard

250 ml (8 fl oz) chicken stock

Serves 2

---

• As oven temperatures vary,
always test the chicken with a
skewer or small knife. If there is
any hint of pink meat juices, then
cook for a further 10–15 minutes
and test again.
• Garlic loses its pungency when
roasted and takes on a lovely
sweetness. Simply peel off the
papery skins and eat whole.

---

**A whole roast chicken can be too much for two people, but roasting joints is more cost effective, quicker and there's less wastage.**

Make 2 slits in each chicken breast and place a bay leaf in each cut. Cut 2 slices of orange, halve each slice and slide a piece under each bay leaf. Put the breasts into a large roasting tin and squeeze the juice from the remaining orange over the chicken. Arrange the vegetables and garlic around the chicken, drizzle with oil and season with salt and pepper. Cover loosely in clingfilm and refrigerate until ready to cook.

To finish, place in a preheated oven, 200°C (400°F), Gas Mark 6, for 50 minutes. Baste the chicken and vegetables, turning them when necessary. Drizzle with honey and cook for a further 10 minutes or until the chicken juices run clear when a skewer is inserted into the thickest part of the breasts, and the vegetables are golden. Lift the chicken and vegetables out of the roasting tin with a draining spoon, reserving the pan juices. Serve with orange wedges and garnished with bay leaves.

To make the gravy, mix the cornflour and mustard with a little cold stock until smooth, then stir in the rest of the stock and season with salt and pepper. Pour the stock into the roasting tin with the pan juices, bring to the boil and boil, stirring, until thickened and smooth. Pour the gravy into a jug and serve with the chicken and vegetables.

## BONUS POINT
• Chicken is a good source of protein and niacin, a B vitamin required for the production of energy in cells, and to maintain a healthy skin and digestive system.

# TUNA & CORN CAKES

250 g (8 oz) potatoes, quartered

15 g (½ oz) butter

grated rind and juice of ½ lemon

100 g (3½ oz) leeks, green part only,
    thinly sliced

200 g (7 oz) can tuna in water, drained

50 g (2 oz) frozen sweetcorn

1 egg, beaten

1 tablespoon semi-skimmed milk

50 g (2 oz) fresh breadcrumbs

1–2 tablespoons sunflower oil

salt and pepper

**Sauce:**

150 g (5 oz) natural yogurt

2 tablespoons chopped parsley

50 g (2 oz) stuffed olives, chopped

Serves 2

• If you don't have any leeks, then chop a small onion and fry it in a little oil before adding to the mash.
• If you're not a fan of olives, then add a few chopped sun-dried tomatoes or extra herbs to the yogurt sauce instead.
• Frozen parsley makes a handy alternative to fresh and can be used straight from the freezer. Buy ready frozen parsley, or chop fresh parsley and pack it into a small plastic container and freeze.

**These chunky tuna fishcakes are delicious with this tangy olive and herb sauce and they freeze well too. Serve with a mixed salad.**

Cook the potatoes in a saucepan of boiling water for 15 minutes, until tender. Drain and return the potatoes to the pan with the butter, lemon rind and juice, and mash well. Meanwhile, steam the leeks for 3 minutes and stir into the mash.

Flake the tuna and stir it into the mash with the sweetcorn and season with salt and pepper. Shape into 4 cakes on a floured wooden board. Chill, if very soft.

Mix together the egg and milk on a plate and put the breadcrumbs on a second plate. Dip each fishcake into the egg mixture, then into the breadcrumbs until coated. Refrigerate until ready to use.

To make the sauce, mix the yogurt in a small bowl with the parsley and olives. Chill until ready to serve.

To finish, heat 1 tablespoon of the oil in a frying pan, add the fishcakes and fry for 5 minutes, turning once, until golden. Add extra oil, if necessary. Serve the fishcakes with the yogurt sauce.

## BONUS POINT

• Yogurt not only helps to keep your digestive system healthy, but can also be used as a soothing cream to treat thrush, a common disorder during pregnancy.

# CHICKEN PUFF PIE

1 tablespoon olive oil

4 skinless, boneless chicken thighs, about 625 g (1¼ lb), cubed

1 small onion, chopped

1 head of fennel, green fronds reserved, cored and roughly chopped

1 garlic clove, chopped (optional)

200 g (7 oz) can tomatoes

150 ml (¼ pint) chicken stock

1 teaspoon caster sugar

375 g (12 oz) ready-made frozen puff pastry, defrosted

flour, to dust

beaten egg, to glaze

salt and pepper

**To finish:**

coarse sea salt

1 tablespoon sesame seeds

Serves 2

---

• The pie filling may be frozen in a small plastic container until ready to use.

• The chicken mixture can be served with rice or new potatoes instead of the pastry.

• Celery, mushrooms or mixed peppers can be used in place of the fennel.

• The pie can be made in 2 x 500 ml (17 fl oz) individual pie dishes, if preferred.

---

**Fennel adds a wonderful, delicate aniseed flavour to this simple tomato-based chicken pie. Serve with a selection of steamed vegetables.**

Heat the oil in a heavy-based saucepan, add the chicken and onion and fry for 5 minutes, stirring, until browned. Add the fennel to the pan with the garlic, if using. Stir in the tomatoes, stock and sugar and season with salt and pepper then bring to the boil, breaking up the tomatoes with the back of a spoon. Cover and simmer for 20 minutes, then remove from the heat and leave to cool.

Spoon the chicken mixture into a shallow 1.2 litre (2 pint) ovenproof pie dish and sprinkle with the reserved green fennel tops.

Roll out the pastry on a lightly floured surface until 2.5 cm (1 inch) larger all around than the top of the pie dish. Cut a 2 cm (¾ inch) wide strip of pastry from around the edge. Moisten the rim of the pie dish with a little water and position the pastry strip on the rim. Brush with beaten egg and place the pie lid on top. Trim the edges, seal the edges well, then flute with a small knife. Brush the top of the pie with egg and sprinkle with sea salt and sesame seeds. Cover loosely with clingfilm and chill until ready to cook.

To finish, place the pie dish on a baking tray and bake in a preheated oven, 200°C (400°F), Gas Mark 6, for 25 minutes, until well risen and golden.

## BONUS POINT

• Dark chicken meat (thighs or drumsticks) contains twice as much iron and zinc as white meat (chicken breasts).

# LEEK & GRUYERE TART

## Pastry:

150 g (5 oz) plain flour, plus extra
  to dust
50 g (2 oz) medium oatmeal
100 g (3½ oz) butter, diced

## Filling:

1 tablespoon olive oil
1 leek, about 200 g (7 oz), thinly sliced
3 eggs
200 ml (7 fl oz) semi-skimmed milk
3 tablespoons single cream
1 teaspoon Dijon mustard
175 g (6 oz) Gruyère cheese, grated
salt and pepper

Serves 3

---

• If you don't have any cream, add
extra milk instead.

• Cheddar, Emmenthal or a
combination of Cheddar and
Parmesan also taste good.

• Add a little chopped ham or
chopped, grilled bacon or sliced
sun-dried tomatoes, if liked.

• Oatmeal adds a lovely nutty
taste and texture to the pastry, but
if you don't have any to hand,
increase the quantity of flour
accordingly.

• Egg-filled tarts and quiches don't
freeze well, but it can be useful to
have an uncooked pastry case
and a bag of grated cheese in the
freezer ready to use.

---

**This deliciously cheesy, leek tart has a crumbly, nutty-tasting oatmeal pastry. Serve it hot or cold with salad.**

To make the pastry, put the flour and oatmeal into a bowl and season with salt and pepper. Add the butter and rub into the flour using your fingertips (or an electric mixer) until it resembles fine breadcrumbs. Add enough cold water to make a smooth dough and mix together.

Lightly knead the dough, then roll it out thinly on a lightly floured surface to fit an 18 cm (7 inch) loose-bottomed, fluted flan tin. Lift the pastry over a floured rolling pin, and use to line the base and sides of the tin. Trim the top and refrigerate for 15 minutes.

Meanwhile, heat the oil in a frying pan, add the leeks and fry for 2–3 minutes, until softened.

In a bowl, beat together the eggs, milk, cream and mustard and season with salt and pepper. Stir in the Gruyère and leeks. Put the flan tin on a baking sheet and pour in the filling. Bake in a preheated oven, 180°C (350°F), Gas Mark 4, for 40–45 minutes, until the pastry is golden and the filling set.

## BONUS POINT
• As with all egg-based dishes, make sure that the filling is well cooked and set before removing from the oven.

# CRISPY CRUMBED COD

**Smart enough to serve to friends yet easy enough to put together midweek, this dish is ideal when you want a proper dinner but haven't the time or the energy to do anything complicated.**

2 cod steaks, each about 175 g (6 oz)

3 tablespoons fresh breadcrumbs

3 tablespoons chopped basil

3 tablespoons freshly grated Parmesan cheese

2 pieces sun-dried tomato, drained and chopped

1 tablespoon olive oil (or from the jar of tomatoes)

grated rind of ½ lemon

salt and pepper

**To serve:**

new potatoes

steamed green beans

Serves 2

Rinse and dry the cod pieces and put them into a shallow ovenproof dish. Mix together the breadcrumbs, basil, cheese, tomato, oil and lemon rind and season with salt and pepper. Spoon the topping over the cod pieces and press into an even layer. Cover loosely with clingfilm and chill in the refrigerator until ready to cook.

To finish, uncover the fish and cook it in a preheated oven, 190°C (375°F), Gas Mark 5, for 20 minutes until the crumbs are crisp and the fish flakes easily. Lift the fish on to plates with a fish slice, spoon the juices around it and serve with new potatoes and green beans.

## BONUS POINT

• Cod is rich in vitamin B12, an important vitamin that works in conjunction with folic acid to help prevent neural defects. Those following a vegetarian diet may need to take a supplement, but talk to your doctor.

• Salmon steaks can also be used in place of cod, if preferred.

• If using a fan-assisted oven, don't forget to reduce the cooking temperatures slightly or the fish will be overcooked.

• 1 fresh tomato can be used instead of sun-dried tomatoes.

• Double or triple recipes if serving to friends.

# STUFFED MUSHROOMS

**This hearty meat-free main course is quick and easy to put together and low in fat too.**

2 large flat mushrooms

1 tablespoon olive oil

1 small onion, chopped

1 courgette, about 200 g (7 oz), diced

1 garlic clove, chopped

2 tablespoons risotto rice, rinsed

200 g (7 oz) can tomatoes

150 ml (¼ pint) vegetable stock

1 teaspoon pesto

4 teaspoons pine nuts

2 tablespoons freshly grated Parmesan
    cheese

salt and pepper

**To serve:**

salad

French bread

Serves 2

Peel the mushrooms and put them into a shallow ovenproof dish. Heat the oil in a saucepan, add the onion and fry for 5 minutes until just beginning to brown. Add the courgette and garlic and cook for 1 minute, then stir in the rice, tomatoes and stock. Season with salt and pepper and simmer for 10 minutes.

Stir in the pesto. Spoon the courgette mixture over the mushrooms. Sprinkle with the pine nuts and Parmesan and cover loosely with foil. When the dish is cool transfer it to the refrigerator until required.

To finish, cook in a preheated oven, 200°C (400°F), Gas Mark 6, for 20 minutes until the mushrooms are cooked through. Serve with salad and crusty bread.

## BONUS POINTS

• Mushrooms are a good source of vitamin B12, important if you are following a vegetarian diet.

• Mushrooms are also rich in protein and potassium, needed to regulate blood pressure and a normal heartbeat.

---

• Hazelnuts, almonds or sunflower seeds could be used instead of pine nuts.

• If you don't have any fresh Parmesan then use a mixture of dried Parmesan and grated Cheddar cheese.

# CREAMY FISH PIE

4 small baking potatoes, about
    500 g (1 lb), cut into large chunks
1 small leek, diced
1 large salmon steak, about 250 g (8 oz)
1 cod steak, about 200 g (7 oz)
300 ml (½ pint) semi-skimmed milk
50 g (2 oz) butter
25 g (1 oz) plain flour
grated rind and juice of ½ lemon
2 tablespoons chopped parsley, plus
    extra to garnish
salt and pepper

Serves 2

- This recipe can be easily doubled or even trebled – ideal if you have children already or want to share supper with friends. Alternatively, freeze the second or third pie for later use. It will keep for up to 6 weeks in the freezer.
- If making the pie for toddlers, remove a portion before adding the lemon rind and salt and pepper.
- The fish pie can be made in individual portions and reheated separately as required.
- Add a combination of fresh herbs, including parsley and tarragon or dill or chives or chervil. Or if you have half a bag of watercress in the refrigerator, chop this up and add it instead.

**This light and creamy salmon and cod pie, topped with a delicious lemon and leek mash, can be made earlier in the day when you don't feel too tired and then reheated when needed. It's ideal if you have young children, as it can be reheated while you read them a bedtime story. Serve with steamed broccoli.**

Cook the potatoes in a saucepan of boiling water for 15 minutes, until tender. Steam the leek for 4–5 minutes, until tender.

Meanwhile, put the salmon and cod into a saucepan with the milk. Bring to the boil, reduce the heat and simmer for 5 minutes. Remove from the heat and leave to cool for a few minutes.

Lift the fish out of the milk, peel away the skin and flake the fish into large pieces. Carefully check for any bones and then set aside, reserving the milk.

Melt half of the butter and stir in the flour. Gradually add the milk and bring to the boil, stirring until thickened and smooth. Add the lemon rind and parsley and season with salt and pepper, then carefully stir in the flaked fish. Spoon the fish mixture into a 900 ml (1½ pint) pie dish.

Drain and mash the potatoes, then beat in the leek, lemon juice and salt and pepper. Spoon the mash over the fish mixture, fluff it up the top with a fork and dot with the remaining butter. Cover loosely with clingfilm and leave to cool, then refrigerate until ready to cook.

To finish, remove the clingfilm, stand the pie on a baking sheet and cook in a preheated oven, 200°C (400°F), Gas Mark 6, for 25 minutes until the top is golden. Garnish with extra parsley and serve.

## BONUS POINTS
- Oily fish, such as salmon, mackerel and herring, contain essential fatty acids that help to form brain tissue in your developing baby.
- Calcium is crucial to the development of a growing baby, therefore it is important to include plenty of dairy produce and other calcium-rich foods in your diet. Our skeleton doesn't actually stop developing until we are 25, so calcium levels are even more crucial for young mums-to-be. Adding semi-skimmed milk is a great way to do this without adding too many fat-laden calories.

# one-pot suppers

There's something very comforting about tucking into a warming casserole or stew. In addition, most casseroles taste better if cooked slowly for a longer period or reheated – a great advantage when your baby needs feeding just before you are about to eat!

## LAMB HOTPOT

**Inspired by the slow-cooked Greek lamb casserole Afelia, which is flavoured with lemon-scented coriander seeds and onions, this version has been topped with sliced potatoes for a hearty main course.**

1 tablespoon olive oil

300 g (10 oz) diced lean lamb, rinsed and dried with kitchen paper

2 small onions, sliced

1 garlic clove, chopped

1 tablespoon coriander seeds, crushed

1 tablespoon plain flour

300 ml (½ pint) lamb stock

4 tablespoons sherry (optional)

salt and pepper

chopped parsley or thyme leaves, to garnish

**Topping:**

325 g (11 oz) potatoes, thinly sliced

2 teaspoons olive oil

few crushed coriander seeds

Serves 2

Heat the oil in a flameproof casserole, add the lamb and onions and fry for 5 minutes, until browned. Add the garlic and coriander seeds and cook for a further minute. Stir in the flour, then add the stock and sherry, and season to taste with salt and pepper. Bring to the boil, stirring.

Thinly slice the potatoes and arrange them so that they overlap on the top of the meat. Season with salt and pepper and drizzle with the oil and a few extra coriander seeds. Cover and cook in a preheated oven, 180°C (350°F), Gas Mark 4, for 1½ hours. Remove the lid of the casserole and cook for 30 minutes until the potatoes are lightly browned. Sprinkle with herbs and serve with steamed shredded cabbage.

### BONUS POINT

• Scrub the potato skins rather than peeling them as most of the nutrients present are just below the skin.

---

• As sherry has such a distinctive flavour, just a little is required to add flavour to slow-cooked casseroles.

• If the potatoes aren't very brown at the end of cooking, cheat. Dot with a little butter and pop under the grill.

• If you don't have a pestle and mortar to crush the coriander seeds, then use a small basin or mug and crush them with the end of a rolling pin.

• The meat mixture can be fried in a frying pan and then transferred to a china casserole dish if preferred.

# PEPPERED PORK

**This slow-cooked casserole is lovely ladled into soup bowls with crusty bread to dunk into the sauce.**

1 tablespoon olive oil

300 g (10 oz) pork shoulder steaks, diced

1 onion, sliced

½ red pepper, cored, deseeded and sliced

½ yellow pepper, cored, deseeded and sliced

½ green pepper, cored, deseeded and sliced

2 garlic cloves, chopped (optional)

1 tablespoon plain flour

200 g (7 oz) canned tomatoes

300 ml (½ pint) chicken stock

75 g (3 oz) chorizo sausage, sliced

300 g (10 oz) new potatoes, scrubbed and halved if large

salt and pepper

chopped parsley, to garnish

Serves 2

Heat the oil in a flameproof casserole dish. Add the pork and onion and fry for 5 minutes, stirring until browned.

Add the peppers to pan with the garlic, if using, and fry for 1 minute. Stir in the flour then add the tomatoes, stock, chorizo and potatoes. Season to taste with salt and pepper. Bring to the boil, cover and transfer to a preheated oven, 180°C (350°F), Gas Mark 4, and cook for 1½ hours. To serve, ladle into bowls and sprinkle with parsley.

## BONUS POINTS
• Peppers change from green to red or yellow as they ripen. Weight for weight, green peppers contain twice as much vitamin C as oranges, while red peppers contain three times as much.
• Potatoes aren't fattening at all, it is the butter and flavourings added to them that pile on the weight. To add 1 kilo of body weight you would need to eat 86 large potatoes!

• Be extra careful while pregnant when buying cured meats such as chorizo and salami and always buy them ready-wrapped and date stamped.
• If you are suffering with morning sickness or heartburn then you may prefer to omit the garlic.
• This casserole freezes well so why not double the amount and eat one half now and freeze the other half for after the baby is born.

# ROAST DUCK WITH SPICED LENTILS

**This is more of a one-dish roast, rather than a one-pot stew, but nevertheless it is simple to prepare and cook. Duck makes a welcome change from chicken and works well with the rustic flavours of the Puy lentils and red cabbage.**

175 g (6 oz) red cabbage, finely shredded

100 g (3½ oz) Puy lentils

1 dessert apple, cored and diced

1 small onion, chopped

6 ready-to-eat, dried, stoned prunes (optional)

300 ml (½ pint) chicken stock

1 tablespoon wine vinegar

1 cinnamon stick, halved

4 cloves

2 duck legs, about 275 g (9 oz) each

salt and pepper

thyme, to garnish (optional)

Serves 2

• Although duck contains much more fat than chicken, it adds richness to the vegetables and lentils cooked beneath it.
• Steamed broccoli and mangetout could also be served with the duck.

Put the cabbage, lentils, apple, onion and prunes, if using, into a shallow ovenproof dish or roasting tin. Pour over the stock, then add the vinegar, spices and salt and pepper to taste.

Arrange the duck joints on a roasting rack and place it over the dish or roasting tin (or improvize with a small cooling rack). Prick the duck skin with a small knife or skewer and sprinkle with salt.

Roast in a preheated oven, 200°C (400°F), Gas Mark 6, for 45 minutes or until the duck skin is crispy and the cabbage and lentils tender. Spoon on to plates, discarding the cinnamon and cloves and serve.

## BONUS POINTS
• Unlike dried beans, lentils do not require soaking before cooking; plus they are a good source of protein and fibre.
• A portion of duck contains twice the level of B vitamins, thiamin and riboflavin as the same-sized piece of chicken.

# LAMB STEW & DUMPLINGS

**There's something wonderfully comforting about this meaty casserole. It's warming, easy to eat with a fork and, if you get delayed, it won't spoil.**

1 tablespoon sunflower oil

250 g (8 oz) lamb fillet, sliced

1 onion, chopped

150 g (5 oz) swede, cubed

150 g (5 oz) carrots, cubed

150 g (5 oz) parsnips, cubed

300 g (10 oz) potatoes, cut into
    large cubes

1 tablespoon plain flour

450 ml (¾ pint) lamb stock

2 rosemary sprigs or a large pinch of
    dried rosemary

100 g (3½ oz) leek, thinly sliced

salt and pepper

**Dumplings:**

75 g (3 oz) self-raising flour

40 g (1½ oz) suet

2 teaspoons finely chopped rosemary
    or parsley

3–4 tablespoons water

Serves 2

Heat the oil in a flameproof casserole dish, add the lamb and onion and fry for 5 minutes, stirring, until browned.

Add the root vegetables and stir in the plain flour. Pour the stock over the lamb and vegetables, add the rosemary and season with salt and pepper, then bring to the boil. Cover the casserole and transfer to a preheated oven, 160°C (325°F), Gas Mark 3, for 1¼ hours or longer, if preferred.

To make the dumplings, put the self-raising flour, suet, rosemary or parsley and salt and pepper into a bowl. Mix in enough water to make a soft but not sticky dough. Shape into 6 balls.

Remove the casserole from the oven and stir in the sliced leek, then add the dumplings. Cover the casserole and return it to the oven for 20 minutes, until the dumplings are well risen and fluffy. Spoon into soup bowls and serve.

## BONUS POINT

• Lamb is high in protein, as well as rich in B vitamins, zinc and iron, important nutrients for your baby.

• The lamb casserole can be frozen, before adding the dumplings, in a plastic box or individual plastic bags. Seal well and label.

• If you don't have a flameproof casserole dish, cook the meat and vegetables in a frying pan and transfer them to an ovenproof casserole dish before putting it in the oven.

• If you are making the casserole in advance, reheat on the hob and add the dumplings to the bubbling casserole. Cover and simmer for 15 minutes.

# BEEF TAGINE

**This Moroccan-inspired dish may have a long list of ingredients but it is easy to make and most of the spices and long-life goods you will probably have already. Colourful and mildly spiced, the stew can be served with warmed Middle Eastern bread or pitta bread.**

1 tablespoon olive oil

250 g (8 oz) extra lean minced beef

1 onion, chopped

125 g (4 oz) swede, diced

125 g (4 oz) carrot, diced

½ teaspoon each of turmeric, ground cumin, cinnamon and mild chilli powder

1 garlic clove, chopped

200 g (7 oz) can tomatoes

300 ml (½ pint) chicken stock

200 g (7 oz) canned chickpeas, drained and rinsed

2 tablespoons raisins or sultanas

75 g (3 oz) frozen broad beans

50 g (2 oz) frozen peas

salt and pepper

torn coriander leaves, to garnish (optional)

Serves 4

Heat the oil in a flameproof casserole, add the beef and onion and fry, breaking up the mince with a wooden spoon, for 5 minutes, until browned.

Stir in the swede, carrot, spices and garlic and cook for 1 minute. Add the tomatoes, stock, chickpeas, raisins and salt and pepper. Bring to the boil, stirring, then cover. Transfer to a preheated oven, 180°C (350°F), Gas Mark 4, for 1½ hours.

Remove the casserole from the oven, add the frozen vegetables and stir well. Return to the oven for a further 10 minutes. To serve, spoon into shallow dishes and sprinkle with coriander.

## BONUS POINT
• Combining a small amount of meat with lots of vegetables and beans helps to keep fat levels down, while the protein, vitamin and mineral content remains high.

• This recipe uses a small pack of mince, but since it is mixed with a plentiful amount of vegetables, it makes 4 good-sized portions.
• The meat mixture can be frozen before adding the frozen vegetables, if liked.
• Serve the tagine with couscous or brown rice instead of bread.
• Minced lamb can be used as an alternative to the minced beef.

# PUMPKIN GOULASH

1 tablespoon sunflower oil

1 onion, roughly chopped

1 red pepper, cored, deseeded and cut
    into chunks

1 garlic clove, crushed (optional)

2 teaspoons paprika

1 teaspoon caraway seeds

375 g (12 oz) pumpkin or butternut
    squash, thickly sliced and
    deseeded

1 large carrot, thickly sliced

75 g (3 oz) red lentils, rinsed

450 ml (¾ pint) vegetable stock

4 teaspoons tomato purée

1 teaspoon light muscovado sugar

salt and pepper

**To garnish:**

4 tablespoons half-fat crème fraîche or
    natural yogurt

paprika

caraway seeds

Serves 2

**Packed with Hungarian flavour, this cheap and tasty pumpkin and lentil casserole can be made in advance and reheated when needed. Serve with chunky slices of bread.**

Heat the oil in a flameproof casserole, add the onion and fry for 5 minutes, until lightly browned. Add the red pepper, garlic, if using, paprika and caraway seeds and cook, stirring, for 1 minute.

Add the pumpkin, carrot, lentils, stock, tomato purée, sugar and salt and pepper. Bring to the boil, cover and cook in a preheated oven, 180°C (350°F), Gas Mark 4, for 1 hour.

To serve, spoon the goulash into bowls then top with a spoonful of crème fraîche and a sprinkling of paprika and caraway seeds.

## BONUS POINTS

• Although lentils are a good source of protein, they do not contain all eight essential amino acids; combining them with vegetables and serving with bread gives a better balance of essential amino acids.

• Brightly coloured vegetables, such as pumpkin, butternut squash, carrots and peppers, contain beta carotene, the plant form of vitamin A, needed for normal cell division and the development of your baby.

• The caraway seeds can be left out, if preferred.

• Make double quantities and freeze half in individual portions for later use.

• Paprika can be bought in two strengths – mild and the much hotter 'picante', which is similar in strength to chilli powder.

# SAUSAGE CASSEROLE

**Simple to make and full of flavour, this budget supper makes a complete meal in one pot. For a meat-free alternative, use vegetarian sausages, vegetable stock and omit the Worcestershire sauce.**

8 chipolata sausages

1 tablespoon sunflower oil

1 onion, chopped

3 carrots, about 200 g (7 oz), cut into
    chunks

2 celery sticks, thickly sliced (optional)

2 small baking potatoes, about
    250 g (8 oz), quartered

1 tablespoon plain flour

400 g (13 oz) can mixed beans, drained
    and rinsed

300 ml (½ pint) chicken stock

1 tablespoon Worcestershire sauce

1 tablespoon tomato purée

2 teaspoons Dijon mustard

2 teaspoons light muscovado sugar

2 bay leaves

salt and pepper

Serves 2

Grill the sausages for 5 minutes, until browned but not completely cooked, then set aside.

Heat the oil in a flameproof casserole, add the onion and fry for 5 minutes, until lightly browned. Add the carrots, celery and potatoes, then stir in the flour.

Add the beans, stock, Worcestershire sauce, tomato purée, mustard, sugar, bay leaves and salt and pepper and bring to the boil. Return the sausages to the pan, cover and cook in a preheated oven, 180°C (350°F), Gas Mark 4, for 1 hour. Spoon into shallow bowls and serve.

## BONUS POINT
• Canned beans are a good source of soluble fibre, protein, B vitamins and starch, which is broken down slowly by the body giving a gradual energy boost and leaving you feeling full for longer.

• If you would rather use dried beans, cook more than required, about 250 g (8 oz), and freeze the rest. Or use a can of baked beans, if preferred.

• Use a slow cooker, if you have one, and refer to the handbook for timings.

• The potatoes can be left out, if liked, but serve the casserole with bread instead.

• This casserole freezes well, but add extra stock when defrosting and reheat thoroughly on the hob or in a microwave.

# EASY ONE-POT CHICKEN

**If you're suffering with constant bouts of nausea, this simple, homely casserole, with just a hint of lemon, will help to boost your flagging energy levels.**

1 kg (2 lb) chicken

1 onion, quartered

3 carrots, about 200 g (7 oz), quartered

2 medium baking potatoes, about 325 g (11 oz), quartered

½ lemon, sliced

bunch of fresh mixed herbs or dried bouquet garni

750 ml (1¼ pints) chicken stock

2 teaspoons Dijon mustard

15 g (½ oz) butter

a little paprika

125 g (4 oz) broccoli, cut into florets

salt and pepper

Serves 2

---

• For an easy chicken soup: strain any remaining stock, adding leftover chicken, finely chopped, and extra finely chopped vegetables, then simmer for 20 minutes.

• Sliced fennel could be added or half a sliced orange, mustard and a small bunch of tarragon instead of lemon and mixed herbs.

---

Put the chicken, breast-side down, into a medium-sized, flameproof casserole. Arrange the onion, carrots and potatoes around the chicken and add the lemon slices and herbs. Mix the stock with the mustard and pour into the casserole. Season with salt and pepper and bring to the boil.

Cover the casserole and transfer to a preheated oven, 180°C (350°F), Gas Mark 4, for 1 hour or until the chicken juices run clear when a skewer is inserted into the thickest part of the leg and breast.

Turn the chicken over. Dot the butter over the breast and legs and sprinkle with paprika. Tuck the broccoli around the chicken, pressing it below the level of the stock. Return to the oven and cook uncovered for 15 minutes, until the chicken is golden and the broccoli tender.

Carve the chicken and arrange in shallow soup bowls with the vegetables and reduced stock.

## BONUS POINTS

• Low in fat and easy to digest, this dish is ideal throughout all stages of pregnancy.

• Salmonella, a food poisoning bacteria sometimes found in chicken, is destroyed by thorough cooking.

# good for you puds

We all love puds, but they can be an easy way to pile on the calories, especially as your pregnancy progresses. But there's no need to keep desserts off the menu, simply have a little of what you fancy and keep the more indulgent puddings for a special treat.

## NO-BAKE LIME & BLUEBERRY CHEESECAKE

50 g (2 oz) butter

2 tablespoons golden syrup

150 g (5 oz) malted milk biscuits, crushed

**Filling:**

250 g (8 oz) mascarpone cheese

200 g (7 oz) virtually fat-free fromage frais

50 g (2 oz) caster sugar, sifted

grated rind and juice of 2 limes

150 ml (¼ pint) double cream

**To decorate:**

250 g (8 oz) strawberries, halved or sliced, if large

125 g (4 oz) fresh blueberries

sifted icing sugar (optional)

Serves 4

---

• Lemon or a combination of lemon and lime or even orange juice could also be added to this pudding.

---

**This tangy cheesecake couldn't be easier to make; there's no gelatine to dissolve, or lengthy cooking times to worry about. Yet the crumbly biscuit base, light, creamy filling and pretty berry topping are sure to tempt the taste buds.**

To make the base, melt the butter and syrup in a saucepan. Put the biscuits in a plastic bag, crush finely with a rolling pin, then stir into the butter mixture. Mix well and press into the base of an 18 cm (7 inch) loose-bottomed, fluted flan tin.

Beat the mascarpone in a bowl to soften, then stir in the fromage frais, sugar and lime rind. Gradually beat in the lime juice.

In a second smaller bowl, whisk the cream until it forms soft peaks, then fold into the mascarpone mixture. Spoon the creamy filling on to the biscuit base and swirl the top with the back of a spoon. Refrigerate for 3 hours or longer, if preferred.

Carefully remove the cheesecake from the tin, decorate with berries and a dusting of icing sugar, if liked.

### BONUS POINTS

• Double cream and mascarpone cheese add the most wonderful flavour to desserts but are high in calories and saturated fat. Add volume, but not at the expense of taste or calories, by mixing with virtually fat-free fromage frais.

• Dairy foods are rich in calcium; vital for your baby's growing skeleton.

• Vitamin C is not stored by the body so is needed on a daily basis. It is also heat-sensitive so serve fruits raw whenever possible for maximum vitamin content.

# PLUM CRUMBLE

**Homely and comforting, this old-fashioned pud is the perfect finale to a Sunday roast dinner. Serve with dollops of fromage frais.**

500 g (1 lb) red plums, halved and
    stoned
50 g (2 oz) light muscovado sugar
3 tablespoons water
fromage frais, to serve

**Topping:**
75 g (3 oz) plain flour
25 g (1 oz) porridge oats
50 g (2 oz) light muscovado sugar
50 g (2 oz) butter, diced
25 g (1 oz) sunflower seeds
25 g (1 oz) sesame seeds

Serves 4

---

• Make double or even triple the quantity of the crumble topping and store in a plastic container in the freezer for up to 3 months; use for a quick midweek pud.
• Vary the fruits in the crumble; rhubarb, gooseberries, apples, pears or fresh peaches also taste delicious.

---

Put the plums, sugar and measured water into a saucepan. Cover and simmer for 5 minutes, until just softened, then transfer to a 1 litre (1¾ pint) ovenproof dish.

To make the topping, put the flour, oats and sugar into a bowl. Rub in the butter using your fingertips until the mixture resembles fine breadcrumbs. Mix in the seeds, then spoon over the fruit mixture.

Bake in a preheated oven, 180°C (350°F), Gas Mark 4, for 30 minutes, until golden. Spoon into bowls and serve warm with spoonfuls of fromage frais.

## BONUS POINTS

• Plums contain vitamin E, an antioxidant that helps to protect cells from damage caused by free radicals and may help to slow down signs of premature ageing, such as wrinkles.
• Seeds contain calcium but in a form that is more difficult for the body to assimilate. Absorption of calcium can be boosted by serving them with foods rich in vitamin C, such as steamed green vegetables or fruit.

# CITRUS CRUSH

**Light and refreshing, this pudding is perfect if you're feeling nauseous or seem to have a permanently strange taste in your mouth.**

125 g (4 oz) caster sugar

150 ml (¼ pint) water

1 pink or ruby grapefruit, scrubbed and halved

2 oranges, scrubbed and halved

1 lime, scrubbed and halved

a few mint leaves, to decorate (optional)

Serves 4

- Serve the Citrus Crush with strawberries tossed with passion fruit seeds.
- Use 2 grapefruits in place of the oranges and lime, if preferred.

Put the sugar and measured water into a small saucepan. Bring to the boil and cook until the sugar dissolves. Remove from the heat and leave to cool.

Squeeze the juice from the fruit. Scoop out the membranes from the fruit shells with a spoon and reserve the shells for serving. Strain the fruit juices into the cooled sugar syrup, then pour into a shallow plastic container to a depth of no more than 2.5 cm (1 inch).

Freeze the citrus mixture for 2 hours, until mushy, then beat with a fork to break up the ice crystals. Return to the freezer for a further 2 hours, beating at 30 minute intervals, until the mixture resembles finely crushed ice.

Scoop the iced dessert into the fruit shells and serve or return to the freezer in a plastic container and use within 3 days.

## BONUS POINTS

- This healthy dessert is completely fat free.
- Citrus fruit is bursting with vitamin C, which is needed to make collagen, a protein essential for healthy gums, teeth, bones, cartilage and skin, and vital for your growing baby.

# STRAWBERRY & LIME BRULEE

**This makes an indulgent alternative to the usual run-of-the-mill fruit yogurt, yet is much easier to make and healthier than the classic brûlée.**

1 teaspoon sunflower oil

4 teaspoons demerara sugar

175 g (6 oz) strawberries, hulled and sliced

1 passion fruit, halved (optional)

200 g (7 oz) Greek yogurt

1 tablespoon icing sugar

grated rind of 1 small lime or ½ small orange

**Serves 2**

• Don't add the sugar topping until the last minute or it will lose that wonderful crunchy texture.

• Vary the fruits depending on what you have in the fruit bowl, such as halved grapes and sliced pears or use a small can of fruit in natural juice, or poached dried fruits in apple or orange juice.

Line a small baking sheet with foil and, with a pencil, draw around the top of two 200 ml (7 fl oz) individual soufflé dishes. Lightly grease the foil. Sprinkle the sugar within the circles and press into an even layer with the back of the spoon. Cook the sugar circles under a preheated grill, placed 5 cm (2 inches) away from the heat, for 4–5 minutes, until the sugar has dissolved and is just beginning to caramelize. Leave to cool.

Divide the strawberries between the dishes. If using the passion fruit, scoop the seeds out of halved shells and spoon over the strawberries. Mix together the yogurt, icing sugar and fruit rind and spoon on top of the fruit. Chill until ready to serve.

Peel the sugar circles off the foil, arrange on top of the yogurt and serve immediately.

## BONUS POINTS

• Strawberries contain more vitamin C than any other berry fruit. In homeopathic medicine, they are thought to cleanse and purify the digestive system and act as a mild tonic for the liver.

• Like blackberries, strawberries contain salicylates, a natural aspirin-like compound. If you react badly to aspirin, then you may also experience an allergic reaction to strawberries.

• Yogurt is a good source of calcium and phosphorus, both of which are essential for strong bones and teeth in your growing baby.

# TANGY GRAPE JELLIES

**Refreshingly light, this delicate pudding is quick and easy to put together and can even be made the night before if preferred. Ideal for the later stages of pregnancy when you would like to finish a meal with something sweet but don't have very much room!**

3 tablespoons cold water

2 teaspoons powdered gelatine

25 g (1 oz) caster sugar

grated rind and juice of 1 lemon

250 g (8 oz) mixed red and white
    seedless grapes, well washed

300 ml (½ pint) sparkling white
    grape juice

**To serve:**

4 tablespoons Greek yogurt with honey

mint leaves

Serves 4

Put the water into a small bowl or mug and sprinkle the gelatine over the top, making sure no dry specks of gelatine are left. Leave to soak for 5 minutes.

Meanwhile, mix the sugar with the lemon rind and juice. Halve the grapes and set them aside.

Stand the gelatine still in a bowl or mug in a small saucepan of hot water and gently simmer for 4–5 minutes, until the gelatine has completely dissolved and become a clear straw-coloured liquid. Stir the gelatine into the lemon and sugar mixture until the sugar has dissolved, then add the grapes and grape juice. Freeze for 15 minutes then pour into four wine glasses (this stops the grapes from sinking) and chill for 3 hours or until set.

To serve, spoon the yogurt on top of the jellies and decorate with tiny mint leaves.

## BONUS POINTS

• 100 g (3½ oz) grapes contain just 60 calories; that's about the same as just one digestive biscuit!

• Grapes are a good source of potassium, which helps to regulate blood pressure and heart beat, so are extremely important for pregnant mums with their increase in blood production.

---

• Gelatine can be dissolved in the microwave for 1½ minutes on medium power, stirring once halfway through cooking. Leave to stand for 2 minutes before continuing with the recipe.

• Jellies can also be set in small moulds and turned out if preferred, but leave for 4 hours so the mixture is firmer before unmoulding.

• Serve with tiny dainty biscuits if entertaining.

• If you have a zester, pare tiny curls of lemon rind off a second lemon and use to decorate the jellies instead of mint.

# SUMMER FRUIT SKEWERS

**Eye catching yet quick to prepare, these fresh fruity kebabs taste delicious threaded on to lemon grass stems and dunked into the low-fat banana and fromage frais sauce.**

4 thin lemon grass stems

400 g (13 oz) strawberries, rinsed
    and halved

3 nectarines or peaches, rinsed, halved,
    stoned and thickly sliced

4 kiwi fruits, peeled and thickly sliced

grated rind and juice of 1 lime

1 medium banana

200 g (7 oz) virtually fat-free
    fromage frais

Serves 4

---

• As the banana discolours with standing, the sauce is best made just before serving or no more than 30 minutes in advance.

• If you are short of time or unable to get lemon grass in your supermarket, simply arrange the fruits on a plate with a bowl of dip in the centre.

• Don't eat lemon grass, it's very chewy unless its finely chopped.

---

Cut the lemon grass stems in half lengthways and peel off the outer grubby leaves. Using the clean stems as skewers, thread strawberries, nectarines and kiwi fruits alternately on to the lemon grass until all the stems have been filled. Put them on to a plate and drizzle the lime juice over the fruit. Chill until needed.

Just before serving, mash the banana with a fork and then stir it into the fromage frais with the lime rind. Spoon the sauce into a small bowl and serve with the fruit skewers.

## BONUS POINTS
• Eating fruits raw is a great way to maximize their abundant supply of vitamin C, carotenes and fibre, especially if you eat them with the skin on.
• Fromage frais makes a low-calorie alternative to cream and can be sweetened with naturally sweet fruits such as banana, as in this recipe, a little honey or a spoonful of icing sugar.

# healthy cakes & bakes

Cooking can be very relaxing, and nothing can be more inviting than the aroma of freshly baked cakes and biscuits. They don't have to be unhealthy either!

## PRUNE & VANILLA MUFFINS

50 g (2 oz) sugar lumps

300 g (10 oz) plain flour

3 teaspoons baking powder

125 g (4 oz) light muscovado sugar

175 g (6 oz) ready-to-eat, dried, stoned
   prunes, roughly chopped

3 eggs

4 tablespoons sunflower oil

50 g (2 oz) butter, melted

1½ teaspoons vanilla essence

150 g (5 oz) natural yogurt

Makes 12

**Big, blowsy and surprisingly light, these muffins are delicious fresh from the oven accompanied by a mug of steaming hot chocolate.**

Line a deep, 12-hole muffin tray with paper cases. Put the sugar lumps into a plastic bag and roughly crush with a rolling pin.

Put the flour, baking powder and sugar into a large bowl, add the prunes and stir to mix. Beat the eggs, oil, melted butter and vanilla in a small bowl and add to the flour mixture. Add the yogurt and stir gently until just combined.

Divide the mixture between the paper cases, sprinkle with the crushed sugar and bake in a preheated oven, 190°C (375°F), Gas Mark 5, for 18–20 minutes, until well risen and the tops have cracked. Serve while still warm.

### BONUS POINT
• Rich in soluble fibre, iron and potassium, prunes add a rich sweetness to these muffins.

• The secret to successful muffins is almost to under-mix them; don't worry too much if there are tiny patches of flour – over-mixing makes them heavy when baked.

• Although muffins can be frozen, nothing beats the flavour of freshly baked muffins and the wonderful aroma that permeates the house.

# SPICED ALL-BRAN BARA BRITH

**This simple tea cake is ideal for the later stages of pregnancy or when you have just had your baby, as its plain, comforting taste and texture help to keep heartburn at bay while giving you a burst of energy too.**

300 ml (½ pint) boiling water

1 teabag

125 g (4 oz) All-bran cereal or other fibre bran cereal

125 g (4 oz) soft light muscovado sugar

250 g (8 oz) luxury mixed dried fruit

1 teaspoon ground cinnamon

½ teaspoon ground allspice or nutmeg

125 g (4 oz) self-raising flour

1 dessert apple, cored, peeled and diced

2 tablespoons semi-skimmed milk or water

2 tablespoons demerara sugar

Makes 10 slices

Pour the boiling water over the teabag and leave to soak for 10 minutes. Squeeze out the bag and discard. Put the cereal, sugar, dried fruit and spices into a bowl. Add the tea and leave to soak for 30 minutes.

Meanwhile, line the base and sides of a 15 cm (6 inch) square cake tin with a piece of nonstick baking paper and snip into the corners so that the paper fits snugly into the base of the tin.

Stir the flour, apple and milk into the All-bran mixture, then spoon into the prepared tin and level with a palette knife. Sprinkle with the demerara sugar and bake in a preheated oven, 180°C (350°F), Gas Mark 4, for 1–1 hour 10 minutes or until a skewer comes out cleanly when inserted into the centre of the cake.

Leave the cake to cool in the tin, then turn it out and peel off the paper. It can be stored in an airtight tin or plastic container for up to 1 week. Cut into thick slices and serve spread with butter or low-fat spread.

## BONUS POINTS

• Constipation is one of the not-so-nice side effects of pregnancy. Try to increase the amount of fibre-rich foods, such as All-bran, pulses, fruit and vegetables, in your diet.
• Drink plenty of fluids during the day, especially if you are increasing the amount of fibre in your diet. Try fruit teas, chilled water or fruit juices and aim for at least 8 glasses a day.

---

• If you don't have an apple, then increase the amount of dried fruit by 50 g (2 oz). In place of the mixed dried fruit, try making your own combination, including chopped dried apricots, cherries, sultanas, currants or whatever you have to hand.

• A mixture of orange juice and semi-skimmed or soya milk, or all milk could be used instead of the cold tea, if preferred.

• If you have 2 x 1 kg (2 lb) loaf tins, then double the quantity of cake mixture. Cook the cakes side by side on the same oven shelf. Freeze 1 cake, wrapped in foil, for up to 3 months; it can be taken into hospital with you to boost energy levels and help to get your bowels moving after the birth.

# STICKY APRICOT MUESLI BARS

**These tasty, chewy flapjack-style bars are made with a mixture of fruit, seeds and oats. They provide plenty of long-term energy, so keep a supply handy to curb sickness and hunger pangs.**

125 g (4 oz) butter

125 g (4 oz) soft, light muscovado sugar

4 tablespoons golden syrup

125 g (4 oz) ready-to-eat, dried apricots, roughly chopped

125 g (4 oz) porridge oats

25 g (1 oz) linseeds

25 g (1 oz) sunflower seeds

25 g (1 oz) sesame seeds

25 g (1 oz) pumpkin seeds

50 g (2 oz) self-raising flour

3 pieces of stem ginger in syrup, drained and chopped (optional)

## Makes 10 bars

---

• You will find all these seeds in large supermarkets and health food shops. Any remaining seeds can be used toasted in salads, added to crumble toppings or ground with a little oil for a tasty spread, rather like peanut butter.

• Muesli can be used instead of the porridge oats.

---

Line the base and sides of a 20 cm (8 inch) shallow square tin with nonstick baking paper and snip into the corners so that it fits snugly.

Melt the butter, sugar and syrup in a saucepan. Stir in the apricots, oats, seeds, flour and stem ginger, if using, and mix well. Spoon the mixture into the tin and press flat. Bake in a preheated oven, 180°C (350°F), Gas Mark 4, for 20–25 minutes, until browned and the edges have darkened.

Leave to cool for 10 minutes, then mark into 10 bars with a knife and allow to cool completely. Remove the bars from the tin. They can be stored in an airtight biscuit tin or plastic container for up to 5 days.

### BONUS POINTS
• Seeds are an excellent source of protein, fibre and unsaturated fat.
• Linseeds – the tiny brown seeds – are an excellent source of omega-3 essential fatty acids, believed to be essential for the early development of the brain and retina of the eye.
• Seeds, particularly pumpkin seeds, contain zinc, which aids reproduction, the immune system and the make-up of DNA.

# Index

# Acknowledgements

**Getty Images** /Image Bank 27, 33, 38, 53, /Stone 44, 46, /Telegraph 34, 41, 49.

**Octopus Publishing Group Limited** /Colin Bowling 30 bottom left, /Jean Cazals 28, /Jeremy Hopley 22 bottom right, /David Jordan 2 top left, 2 centre, 2 top right, 2 bottom right, 2 bottom left, 4–5, 8, 11 bottom left, 13 bottom right, 13 bottom left, 19 top left, 19 top right, 19 bottom right, 19 bottom left, 19 centre left above, 19 centre left below, 19 centre right above, 19 centre right below, 20, 21 left, 21 right, 26 top right, 29, 31 top left, 32, 36, 42, 48, 54 left, 54 right, 55 left, 55 right, 56 left, 56 right, 57 left, 57 right, 58, 61, 62, 64, 66, 69, 71, 73, 74, 77, 79, 81, 82, 84, 86, 89, 91, 93, 97, 99, 100, 103, 105, 107, 109, 110, 112, 115, 116, 118, 123, 125, 127, 129, 131, 132, 134, 139, 141, /William Lingwood 12 top right, 23, 30 top right, 137, /Peter Pugh-Cook 10, 51 top left, 51 centre left, 51 top right, 51 centre right, 51 bottom right, 51 bottom left, /William Reavell 31 bottom, 95, /Simon Smith 12 bottom left, 22 centre left, /Ian Wallace 11 top right, 24, 25.

**Mother and Baby Picture Library** 6, 18, /Ian Hooton 15, 45, 52, /Sean Knox 37, /Paul Mitchell 16, 39, /Steve Shott 35 top left, 35 bottom right.

**Science Photo Library** /CNRI 26 top left.

Executive Editor:
    **Nicola Hill**
Senior Editor:
    **Sarah Ford**
Executive Art Editor:
    **Peter Burt**
Designer:
    **Jo Tapper**
Picture Researchers:
    **Zoë Holtermann**
    **Jennifer Veall**
Production Controller:
    **Viv Cracknell**

Special Photography:
    **David Jordan**
Home Economist:
    **Sara Lewis**
Stylist:
    **Claire Hunt**
Indexer:
    **Hilary Bird**